In
The
Newborn
Year

Elisabeth Brutto Hallett

Cover and text design by Barbara McNew

Library of Congress Cataloging in Publication Data
Hallett, Elisabeth Brutto, 1947-
In the newborn year : our changing awareness after childbirth /
  Elisabeth Brutto Hallett
  p. cm.
Includes index. ISBN 0-913990-87-6 : $10.95
    1. Mothers—United States—Psychology. 2. Motherhood—United States—Psy-
chological aspects. 3. Childbirth—United States—Psychological aspects. I. Title.
  HQ759.H188 1992
  306.874'3—dc20   91-42328
                                                                              CIP

ISBN 0-913990-87-6

*Acknowledgements for the reprinting of previously published material
can be found on pages 216-217.*

0 9 8 7 6 5 4 3 2 1

Dedicated, with love, to my son Devin

Table of Contents

Introduction

Our firstborn son was three weeks old when I wrote, with a feeling of mingled regret and relief, "Fortunately, most of the intense effects are over now." After Devin's birth, my awareness changed in ways I never anticipated. I had tried to prepare for birth and motherhood, but no book or article or friend explained all that happened in those first three weeks. Something had been left out of common knowledge—where did I fit in? Did other new parents go through changes like these? I needed to know; so when Devin was four years old, I began gathering other people's stories:

> "Mothers, fathers, did you have unusual experiences, altered states of awareness in hours, days, weeks following birth or adoption of a child? Please consider participating in private research project ... "

Hundreds of people responded to my request; many completed the long, soul-searching questionnaire, sharing some of the most intimate moments of their lives. I never found another experience exactly like my own, but often felt a shiver of recognition at familiar details. Through each story I glimpsed the mysterious world of "newborn time," our first year with a new baby.

I had hoped to answer a question: was I alone in my experiences during the newborn year? The answer turns out to be both yes and no. Each person's story is different, but recurrent themes connect them. I've learned that the entire year after childbirth is a unique time of change and potential; our response to it is as individual as we are.

Most of the accounts so generously shared with me are from birth mothers. They are people who felt that what happened to them following childbirth was unusual or unexpected. Thus, their stories amplify changes of awareness that for many people may pass almost unnoticed; they reveal the patterns and possibilities during the newborn year.

If you're preparing for a child, these stories will help you think past pregnancy, past labor and delivery and the amazement of a new baby, to the possibility that you—the familiar self you know so well—may be changed. The differences may be slight and fleeting, or so profound that you will say, "I am not the same person."

For partners of new mothers, these stories offer insight into moods and changes that may not be easily explained as one goes through them. (Many of these experiences are in fact shared by fathers.) For birth attendants and others assisting in newborn time, they reveal the special needs and vulnerabilities of mothers and families.

The principal event of this time is the meeting of parent and baby. The shock waves that result from this encounter ripple through us in the form of emotions, insights, and feelings about the connection we have with this new person. The stories of Part I focus upon this central bond.

For myself, the bond with my new baby was unexpected and thrilling. But even more surprising were the experiences of the following weeks. They seemed to reveal an unsuspected power in this stage of life—a power to transform awareness. Part II, "A Diary of Newborn Time" is the day-to-day record of my own impressions during that time.

Perhaps no other life crisis has such an impact on us as the transition to parenthood. In response to it we may experience altered states of mind, a new range of emotion, even changes in sensory perception. The stories of Part III explore these and other changes of awareness that may overtake us during the year after childbirth.

In this newborn year people often seem more open to the subconscious mind, and possibly to other dimensions of reality as well. Powerful dreams, visions, and apparent psychic experiences abound. The stories of Part IV follow these marvelous and sometimes frightful adventures through other doors of awareness.

While gathering accounts of the newborn year, it was always moving to read, "I've never told anyone . . ." or "I've wondered if this has happened to anyone else." This book may assure people who experience unusual events and states of mind that they are not alone. I hope these stories will make it easier to talk about happenings that are part of the fabric of our lives, but are so often hidden from each other.

Above all I hope they will increase our ability to protect and enjoy the newborn year. It is a fragile and powerful time, when changes in awareness present both opportunity and danger. By sharing our experiences we will be better able to recognize these changes, to prevent the pain that results from ignoring and mishandling them, and to foster their life-enriching potential in ourselves and one another.

Elisabeth Brutto Hallett

In
The
Newborn
Year

Part I

MEETING OUR NEW BABY

The Central Bond

"*N*ewborn time," our first year with a new baby, doesn't exist in isolation but is part of the continuing story of our lives. The pivotal event, the bonding of parent and child, doesn't always happen just at birth. Some parents sense a definite connection with their babies long before they're born; for others, the bond develops later. And for all parents, it alters over time as we and our children change and grow.

Sandra's story places this central bond—and the newborn year itself—into a longer perspective, touching on many aspects of changing awareness in the cycle of pregnancy, birth and parenthood.

Sandra Ure Griffin is an artist and writer; her first children's book, *Earth Circles* (Walker & Co.), was published in 1989. She is also the mother of four sons, ranging in age from three months to eight years old. "In 1979," she writes, "an onrush of events occurred":

> I became pregnant, I married the man I had been living with for two years, I graduated from the Kansas City Art Institute, we signed a twenty-year mortgage for a house and fourteen acres in the Ozark foothills, I experienced death firsthand when my brother (age seventeen) was killed in a car accident, I experienced birth with the arrival of my first son, my husband was laid off from his job never to be called back, and, just before the close of that tumultuous year, our house burned to the ground.
>
> Since that time, we rebuilt a log house on the old foundation, and within it greeted three more sons. All of our children were born at home with just my husband and myself in attendance.
>
> My experiences began at conception. I always suspected that I had conceived when I would feel a shift in consciousness accompanied by a subtly throbbing presence, emanating like a warm glow from deep within my womb. This sounds explicit, but really it was a very faint sensation, and one that I was not aware of at all unless I was very still and quiet and tuned into it, like lying in bed in darkness.

Sometime during early pregnancy I would then experience what I can only describe as a "doubling of consciousness," an unusual feeling in which I would become aware that I was no longer one entity, but two, although the second presence was very different, as though I was a flame and it a spark. Again this was a very mild feeling, though it might have been related to the queasiness of morning sickness. Perhaps it is difficult for a body to adjust to the presence of two souls—as well as two physical systems.

During the last few weeks of pregnancy I experienced an extreme narrowing of consciousness, an almost complete centering of my awareness on the coming child. My thoughts seldom strayed away from the baby. When I had to concentrate on other things, an awareness of the baby loomed large behind every thought, forming the same background in my mind at all times.

One evening, when I was only a matter of days from my due-date, I remember driving home from a writers' meeting with a friend. She was trying to discuss the meeting, and I was totally unable to carry on the discussion at any depth. A few sentences only, and my mind would take leave of the subject and return to The Child. It wasn't that I wanted to talk about the baby, it was just that my mind was most comfortable resting upon an awareness of it, kind of like my arms were most comfortable resting on my distended abdomen. My mind was like a determined bird, refusing to leave the egg until it hatched.

In *Spiritual Midwifery* ,* there is much talk of psychedelic feelings increasing as birth becomes imminent. In the birth stories in that book, the mother-to-be feels psychedelic, she looks it, the room around her looks it.

Particularly with my last pregnancy, I really felt an increase in such feelings. The morning before my fourth son was born, I awoke to feel a definite shift in consciousness. I felt, well, trippy, kind of removed from my body a step or two, and my house looked rosy and more colorful than usual. "Gee, I really do feel psychedelic today," I remember saying to myself. "I wonder if the baby will be born tonight." He was.

Each of my four births was profoundly moving, and very mind-altering in a spiritual sense. None was more so than the first, however. I'll quote now from a birth story I wrote for "The New Nativity" newsletter, eight years ago when my first child was six weeks old.

Daylight was breaking. As the dim room began to fill with morning light, we both felt we could sense the child's coming presence . . .

*(Book Publishing,1990)

The universe had become the sensation of one big push. The child was inches away from joining us in this world. My heart was pounding. My husband looked electrified . . .

Without waiting for another contraction, I gave another push, and then whoosh! Our son was in his father's arms, swirling and shining, his rainbow body glowing pink and gray, purple and blue . . .

My husband's priceless, passionate words, "Oh God, it's a baby!" And mine, "A boy!"

I leaned back in ecstasy. He was still quite purple but I knew he would breathe, for the room was glowing with God's presence. His tight grimace began to relax as he gave a few hesitant and shallow breaths, and as his breathing grew stronger he began to pinken.

He had made it to us! He was here! Alive, beautiful, perfect! We looked at each other, unbelieving. We were shaken by the miracle, we had been rocketed together into an ecstatic awareness of God's presence and the proof was right here between us: this new being, our son . . .

I sank back into the pillows, holding his damp little body, feeling totally relaxed and relieved, yet still elated and amazed. I felt like I could have sat there forever, all was perfection and total completion.

I stared into the fresh little eyes and felt a sudden, strong and deep-seated sense of wonder—for somehow I deeply felt an inexplicable recognition for the child. I felt like I could see an infinite chain of ancestors behind those eyes, and he was the newest link and was right in his place. I recognized him as being just the one I was waiting for, as if I had seen him before and had known him all along.

"Oh, of course . . . it's you!"

That initial bonding developed into a very close and intense nursing relationship. I nursed all my children, but the bond was not as all-encompassing as it was with the first.

I was deeply in love with the baby. Romantic interests in my husband diminished for many months, because, I think, I was so wrapped up in my newfound love for our son.

I experienced an unmistakable link with my baby's mind. When sleeping beside me, he would awaken if I stared at him, or if I was thinking about him "too loudly." While nursing him to sleep, I would grow sleepy myself waiting for him to drop off. I came to realize that his eyes were closing in sleep only when mine were, and were flashing open as I opened mine. I learned to drift off into sleep for only a few moments, as if I was leading his mind into sleep, and then returning to consciousness after he settled into a dream. I did spend many an evening falling asleep for the night at 6:30 P.M.!

At times I felt truly at one with my child. I would lie on the bed beside him, looking around the room, blinking occasionally, feeling exactly as if I was seeing things with his eyes. One morning I found myself pushing my face and cheeks into my pillow, feeling just like an infant, like I was either experiencing the thoughts of my baby, or tapping some primal memory from my own infancy.

A few weeks or months after my children were born, I always experienced a brief period of very profound sadness. I don't know if this was a "postpartum depression" brought on by hormonal changes or what. It always saddened me that our world seemed so limited, while in comparison the newborn's eyes glowed with limitless potential. I felt so silly offering a small plastic toy to my child's outstretched fingers, like giving a meaningless trinket to God incarnate. It just seemed that as the baby grew, becoming more and more accultured, he was leaving something behind that was far more important. It was saddening to know that the shining, open trust of the newborn would end up hidden under the shrewdness, arrogance and cynicism of adulthood.

My sadness was also a heightened awareness of the transience of life. Those first few days with my newborn, time seemed to stand absolutely still: it was just the two of us in rapture. Then one morning I woke up and heard a rattling sound from the baby's crib. I had strung some rattle-filled plastic horses across the crib, and this morning, for the first time, my baby had learned to kick the toys and produce the rattle.

Minutes passed, longer and longer, as he continued kicking. He was playing, I realized, playing without me. For the first time he didn't want me, not my milk, or to be changed, or simply held close. I was delighted by his growth, but also infinitely sad. His path would lead one day to complete independence from me, and for each step I would need to let go a little more and a little more.

The startling mind-link that I experienced with the newborns seems to diminish as each child grows older. The feeling of mental one-ness is now a rarity with my smart and worldly almost-eight-year-old, but I do have occasional contacts with my younger ones, both of whom are adept at inexplicable mind-reading.

I'll be scrubbing out pans at the sink, staring out the kitchen window into the spring sunshine. It sure would be nice to go to the river today, I'll think to myself with a sigh.

In toddles three-year-old Jonathan. "Are we going to the river, Mama?" he asks excitedly.

This happens at least once every couple of months. Out-of-the-blue questions or statements that seem snatched from the inner folds of my mind, like the pennies and safety pins they fish from my shirt pockets. Prodding reminders from my grubby-faced drippy-nosed offspring that we were once One and will one day return.

~　　~　　~

I spent hours and hours holding her
and nursing and wondering how the
baby and I could be so separate and
so connected at the same time
- Anara

As we come to know our child through pregnancy, birth and parenthood, we experience both our separateness and our deep connection to this new person. A baby is never really part of her mother's body. She has her own genetic design and private bloodstream, and grows herself within the womb. But to contain another person entirely inside oneself is mind-boggling! It opens a mother's senses to a new kind of awareness, a connection to an inner, unseen dimension where two people can almost be one.

Perhaps this deepened awareness makes way for some of the unusual experiences of the newborn year. There are moments and feelings that reveal the special qualities of the bond between parent and baby. Anara Williams remarks:

For the first few months, I was remarkably stupid about pronouns. If I was asked, "How's the baby?" I'd be likely to answer, "I'm fine." Likewise, if asked about myself I'd reply about him. It wasn't so much being unable to separate our two states of being as that I truly did not hear which pronoun was used—or so I thought at the time. Now I wonder . . .

During her third pregnancy, Valerie tried "to stay closely connected to the baby." Her conscious attention ripened into remarkable experiences at birth and afterwards, and "the absolutely overwhelming feeling of love." She writes:

We had real bad marital problems while I was pregnant with Abbey. My husband seemed to reject me, the kids and the pregnancy, so I tried very hard to stay closely connected to the baby and provide her with lots of extra love and good stuff. Although I felt blessed to have her around, I was really depressed and hurt from our problems and she wasn't growing well. (My doctor said the placenta wasn't putting out.) We wanted to birth her at home, but we decided on a hospital because of her very slow growth. They didn't think she would make it through a long labor.

Now, I don't know what the physical cause of labor is, but this labor was a function of the will and love for Abbey to have a gentle birth. Labor started on a Monday morning. I had gentle contractions every ten minutes until she was born on Thursday afternoon. The waters didn't break until she was headed down the birth canal. What a soft birth! We named her Abbey (joy of the father) Althea (the healer). Our marriage was healed by the appearance of this magical child. Boy, does this sound corny or what?

Abbey was small, but strong. Very strong. But she needed some meat on her bones. So every time I nursed her, I would try to nourish her with my whole being. And every time I did, I would feel our bodies merge into one: body, mind and soul.

One night, after the kids went to bed, I sat down in my favorite chair to nurse the baby. As I stared into her beautiful brown eyes, they became infused with golden light. I didn't break eye contact with her. Was it purity, love, innocence, God, knowledge or goodness? Was it her soul? It was beautiful! She was about two weeks old. Glowing eyes! Golden eyes!

Now she's chunky. She eats like a pig. Like a little kid. That connected feeling doesn't happen any more. But we're still connected!

After nine months of sharing one space, a woman may feel a shock of separation from her baby. Staying close to the newborn can ease this transition. "I couldn't stop staring at Abraham," writes Elizabeth Green. "And my husband seemed to sense my need for still being physically close to him. The minute we got home he moved his bassinet right next to the bed."

The physical bond is so strong that sometimes one hallucinates the baby's presence. Anne Calajoe recalls:

For about two months after the birth of my son, I would sit up in bed in the middle of the night—searching frantically under the sheets for my son because I was afraid he would suffocate. My husband would reassure me he was okay and he was in his cradle next to our bed. Then I would be relieved and go back to sleep.

It was very frantic and intense—I was almost afraid he would disappear. I think it was a form of separation anxiety and working through that the baby was no longer a part of my body, but a separate individual.

Anne's explanation seems logical, and yet Lisa, an adoptive mother, describes an identical experience:

> Although he never slept in our bed but next to it, I always had the sensation that he was with me, or physically next to me. I was very often startled out of a deep sleep because I could feel him in my arms (he was not) and I was afraid he'd fall out of bed. Or that he'd been in my arms (he hadn't) and had wriggled out—just to find him sleeping peacefully in his bed.
>
> I also feared that I'd lack some sort of cosmic connection not having given birth to him. But I couldn't believe how aware and how connected to him I felt.

Patricia is another adoptive mother who was surprised by the deep bond she felt with her baby:

> Every so often I am stunned by his continued state of joy and a feeling of unreality about his being in my life. I feel like he has *always!* been part of my life—the connection feels so deep. We have colds simultaneously—even poop at the same time. The huge connectedness between the two of us amazes me. I am knit to my child.

Not only mothers experience such feelings. In *Spiritual Midwifery*, Daniel describes his sense of being "one thing" with his baby:

> When Nathan was about five days old, a far-out thing happened. I was lying on the bed with him on my stomach. As he started to doze off I could feel his aura opening up, and he kept opening up to where he merged right into me. He was just like a lump on the old log. It was so stoned I just lay there real still for about twenty minutes being one thing with him.

Richard Myers's unusual experience began just before his first son Jesse was born:

> Pam was in transition and I began to feel very "high." It was more intense than anything I've ever imagined possible. It was as though I was now on a different plane of awareness.
>
> As soon as I caught him, it was as if we were one person. I thought that I was feeling what he was feeling. We were communicating on a telepathic and empathetic plane. All we had to do was look into each others' eyes and no words were necessary. He appeared to be able to understand me, and I knew he could.
>
> The strong telepathy lasted for several weeks, and is still somewhat present even now, and he is five years old. Jesse and I have

always had a very special awareness. For many months he would sleep his best when he was tucked under my arm. He could even let me know he needed me when I was asleep.

I never knew how close a parent and child could be. I never knew people could be so close. It's wonderful! I have an awareness, many awarenesses, now that I did not have before. I feel more empathetic responses; I feel much more spiritually whole.

We seem connected to our children by a triple cord of shared inheritance, shared experience and something more, as Robin Kristufek suggests:

"The most unusual and memorable experiences for me were at about two or three days postpartum. I think this is when hormone changes are most intense, having to do with the coming in of the milk. I felt very strongly that my son and I were/are spirits intertwined on this earth, very bonded for our trip together here. I felt our similarity, the fact that we have similar genes, direct evolutions of each other. I felt a past and future, with us simply here now by chance. The infiniteness of the earth, the universe—I felt it in us strongly."

~   ~   ~

Meeting our new baby can be an event that marks a far-reaching change in our lives. It can bring perceptions that dissolve old ways of thinking; like a seed crystal, it can impart a whole new order. For many parents, the feelings of closeness and connection with their newborn are both unexpected and transforming. Says Holly Sink:

At Nikolas' birth I felt as if God was with me, but not God the way most people say that they see God (white light and all). This was much different. Maybe it wasn't God, maybe it was Nickel's soul . . .

It was as if something walked out of the best part of my own soul and became another soul, and turned and touched me. The touch was so soft and yet so deep that it burned. The way some people say they are born with a child, I felt a deep change in me; maybe that's the birth or rebirth that people speak of.

My baby had a lot of trouble and we had to go C-section. That hurt me a little, but that was lost the moment my husband handed me our son. My husband was crying and looking so happy. I just felt the burn of love, of a touch I can't put into words but I can still feel it, I can even see it!

I never thought we would be so connected. My feelings were much stronger than I expected. I think it proved to me that motherhood is so special and that I really would be good at it.

Now and then, the meeting of parent and newborn will open something deep inside that has been closed off.

"The birth of my third child changed my life and my feelings about
family, pregnancy, childcare and numerous other things entirely," says
Nancy. "I suddenly felt like a very different person after the birth, and in the
days that followed I felt that I was truly a *feeling* person for the first time in
my life!" She continues:

> The births of my first two children were typical hospital births and
> my feelings after having them were that I truly never wanted to
> become pregnant again. In my memory, childbirth was a shocking,
> frightful event that was only fit to be shoved into the farthest
> reaches of my mind and (hopefully) forgotten.
>
> Bonding was nonexistent with my first child (I barely even held
> her during the four-day hospital stay) and I functioned very "auto-
> matically" with her for years thereafter. I felt a very slight brush
> with the bonding experience with my second child when I finally
> held him the day after he was born. This "feeling" really took my
> breath away—it was such a wonder to me to have a sweep of
> feeling for a brand-new baby. The fact that he was *my* baby didn't
> diminish the surprise I felt over having experienced this very deep
> something when I held him in my arms.
>
> When my second child was four years old, my husband began
> talking about having another baby. I wasn't too keen on the idea,
> but I wasn't totally against it either. I decided not to think about the
> possibility of pregnancy and just go with the flow of whatever
> happened.
>
> Well, I soon became pregnant and I was terrified. My mind
> screamed No! every time I saw a big-bellied pregnant woman.
> Some part of me totally rejected what was to be my fate within nine
> months. I was unable to read or talk about anything concerning
> childbirth right up to my eighth month of pregnancy.
>
> I am the type of person who can accept the dark things in life
> with an attitude of, "I'm dreading this experience and wish I didn't
> have to do it, but let's do it and get it over with." When something
> must be faced, I can face it fairly calmly and I don't tend to run
> from the things I know I must do.
>
> This is how I felt when my labor started. It was just something I
> had to get through, so I wanted to handle it as best I could.
> Thankfully it was a fast and relatively easy labor.
>
> We had our third baby in a birthing center run by three mid-
> wives. Brenden was overdue and had meconium in his waters. His
> breathing was shallow and the midwives worked over him for an

hour, making sure he was okay, before I ever saw him fully or held him. Somehow I knew my baby was okay, but I basically felt pretty detached from the child as I lay on the bed waiting while the midwives did all they had to do.

I was thoroughly enjoying a blissful, dreamy state of complete and contented happiness. I couldn't stop smiling! This was a totally new experience for me, as I am generally not a very happy or "up" type of person. I had never felt inexplicable happiness like this. I was still marveling over this wonderful state of being (which began actually during the final stage of the birth), when Brenden was put into my arms.

When I looked into his eyes for the first time, an hour or so after he was born, I saw directly into his soul. It was simultaneously a solemn and joyous moment. I saw Brenden's intelligence, which was very fresh and beautiful—untouched—and I saw his fear. I know now that his first hour of life had been fearful for him. I've wondered over what he may have seen when he looked so intently at me—he certainly was looking for something. About all I can say is that in that moment we made a deep, soul-to-soul contact which I've never before, or since, experienced.

To be truthful, I never knew such contact between human beings was possible.

So you see, this experience opened a door to possibilities I never before knew existed. I would go so far as to say that it was a sacred moment.

The months that followed were still colored by a sweet, contented happiness that intensified momentarily every time I looked into Brenden's eyes. It was very much like falling in love—but much, much nicer because of the purity of a newborn baby. Even today, after two years, I experience occasionally the lingering sweetness of those initial postnatal months.

You could easily say that Brenden's birth saved something in me. I believe that it softened me. I can be a very bitter person.

It is clear to me now that birth—though difficult—can be, and probably was designed to be, an awakening experience for a woman. It can surely expand her consciousness and sense of caring and kindness, as nothing else can, that I know of.

Though the dreamy-like state of happiness wears off after a period of time, it leaves you a changed person. How fortunate I feel for having had such an experience.

~   ~   ~

While stories of immediate closeness are beautiful, in fact parents sometimes find that their first reaction to a new baby includes a certain detachment. Pat Turgon recalls:

> Immediately following my first child Jesse's birth I was filled with curiosity, hardly believing this being had really just emerged from me. But I had a sense of detachment and worried why I wasn't filled instantaneously with "motherlove," especially after having had a perfect homebirth.
>
> Jesse was born with the first pink lights of dawn, just as I'd imagined it would be, and throughout that day I had flashes of union and similarity with women everywhere, wondering who else was holding a new baby. I also remember thrilling to the realization that this tiny Jesse trusted *me!* implicitly. Truthfully said though, it was almost exactly three weeks before I suddenly, tearfully knew in my heart of hearts that I would die for this child, would give anything for him.

In her book, *Psychological Effects of Motherhood: A Study of First Pregnancy* (Praeger Publishers, 1980), Myra Leifer studied first-time mothers. She found that they "commonly expressed guilt at not feeling immediate and intense love for their babies," and gives this example:

> A woman who rapidly developed intense bonds with her baby said on the first postpartum day: "I have found it hard to sort out my feelings about her. I have felt exhausted, sore from the stitches, perhaps more focused on myself than on her right now. And that makes me feel very guilty. I have the sense that a good mother should feel a lot of love toward her baby, and I really can't say that what I feel is love. I'm a little frightened of her, I'm also delighted by her and find that I would like to just watch her and get to know her, but in all honesty I can't say that I feel like a mother yet."

Sometimes there is an element of detachment that feels right, allowing us to do things in our own time. After my daughter's birth she was brought alongside me, and I simply looked at her. Then the nurse said, "Touch her." Obediently I reached over and touched fingertips to her chest—but in *my* rhythm, it was not yet time for touching. It was still time just to look. It can be difficult to respect our own rhythm. We ourselves, and well-meaning others like that nurse, want to hurry past the curiosity and get quickly to the love--and that may take some time.

There may be many reasons for an initial sense of detachment. It can be a way of coping with great pressures and conflicting impulses, or a reaction to the overwhelming sensory and emotional events of labor. At times, a feeling of detachment may be a necessary protection. Reflecting on her own experiences, Cynthia Cournoyer came to view it in this way:

When my daughter was born (after thirty-four hours of labor) I did not react in any of the ways I expected to.

During labor I lost all sense of measurable time. I seemed to have tunnel vision. Nothing else existed except the very small area around my body. When she was actually lying there just born, the tunnel vision was intensified. The edges grew dark and all attention was on her.

I was surprised at my reaction to her not breathing right away. I "should" have been worried or panicked. But I was neither. I was sort of numb. I knew things were being done to help her breathe but I felt somehow detached. I didn't want to just grab her up right away. But after I saw her moving around I asked if I could have her.

Looking back over the birth experience in the following days, I became quite guilty at the idea that I should have felt much greater concern for my own child's well-being. I thought there was something wrong with me. I mentioned it to our midwife and she said it was quite normal for women to feel very differently directly after the birth than they would otherwise. This made me feel better about it but it remained a puzzle to me. "Falling in love" with my baby didn't come as naturally as I expected it to. I had to work harder to allow the natural bonding to have a deeper and deeper effect on me.

I have since resolved the whole thing in my mind by figuring that it is a built-in protective mechanism for a new mother. In the stressed state of a woman's body after childbirth, it might be dangerous if she were to lose her mind over the fact that her baby may have been born dead or badly deformed. Nature's built-in defense allows her to accept it gradually.

How about when your baby looks nothing at all like what you had imagined? An adoptive father confessed, "I had some mixed feelings upon seeing my son for the first time. I remember thinking he was ugly and wondering whether it was too late to back out of the adoption." The numbness that parents can feel may be the natural first reaction to loss—the loss of their imagined child.

Risa prepared herself for the birth of her first baby with unusual care. She considered the pregnancy and birth "perfect," yet suffered depression in the following weeks. Perhaps in part she was mourning the baby girl who had become so real to her through her loving attention in pregnancy:

I really worked hard for a perfect birth. I kept in good shape by exercising and walking every day. When I walked I would say an affirmation I made on what kind of birth we would have, how healthy the baby would be and how happy we would be to have him/her.

During the last few months of pregnancy I could feel a presence of someone watching me, just being there. I meditated, relaxed, every day. I was told a number of times how aware and centered I'd become. I read everything I could and talked to a lot of people. I felt good and in control of myself and the birth. I was "prepared."

I had a nurse midwife and delivered in a birthing room at a hospital. Our labor was almost three and a half hours from start to finish. I never felt out of control and never wanted drugs of any kind. As soon as our son was born I had him handed to me and placed on my bare skin. When the cord stopped pulsating Gary cut it. All my sisters, niece, and parents got to hold him. Gary gave him a warm bath. I tried to nurse him right away but it took us a little while. We were never separated from each other except once when they did the PKU and bilirubin tests (which I won't leave my next one for). The birth was a very positive experience for Gary and me.

When he first came out I was in sort of a shock state. I really thought I was having a girl, and he really didn't look anything like I had imagined.

My postpartum depression, which I was totally unprepared for, started on the second day. I felt very detached and an overwhelming sense of responsibility . . .

In the following weeks Risa was haunted by dreams of loss, and frightening episodes of "sleep paralysis"—waking to a sense of threat and helplessness. Looking back, she recognizes that she was under some stress because she had put herself in a situation where she thought she had to be perfect. It seems we can never be totally prepared, nor fully in control. Trying to plan too much may even draw an opposing reaction from the subconscious mind.

Long after loving feelings have replaced any initial detachment, the memory of that coolness can still cause pain. It was six months after her second baby's birth when a mother wrote:

It has taken me this long to accept and begin to forgive the way I failed her in her first few days. She looked so totally different from how I expected her to look, and so funny, just like a pink piglet with her turned up, squared off nose, no neck, no chin to speak of, plenty of jowls and lots of soft folds of extra skin and padding over the back of her shoulders (where I expected a neck to be). Little Quasimodo, I secretly called her. And it has bothered me all this time that I actually said aloud on her second day, "She's as ugly as can be!" How can I forgive myself?

I was petrified at the possibility that this was going to be a really homely child and that perhaps my love was going to turn out to depend upon physical beauty. It was such a scary and humiliating discovery about myself, that it was several days before I really started to feel close to her instead of rather cool and distant. I still recall that moment when I looked over toward where she lay sleeping in the bassinet, and I felt my heart warm to her, an actual sensation. As my love for her increases, I have come to the point of being able to forgive myself and see the funny side of those first few doubt-filled days.

When parents have fallen madly in love with a newborn (often but not necessarily the first), they may experience a letdown with the next baby. This can create anxiety, for we tend to measure the value of our feelings according to their intensity.

Perhaps only with the first baby can there be that unreserved surrender to the new parent-baby romance. When my own second child was born, I identified so strongly with the feelings of my six-year-old that I held back a little from the new baby, out of loyalty to my "first love."

Only the first baby makes one a mother. Part of my delight in my firstborn was falling in love with myself as "mother." With my second baby there was an ordinariness, no extra glamour added to the relationship. I came to appreciate this as a truer response to her—but it was worrisome at first.

As another woman said, for her second baby she felt "less passion, more calm acceptance." Both child and parents may benefit from this less intense beginning. It may signal a more mature stage of parenthood. A mother writes:

I felt a deep affinity and symbiosis with my first child immediately. This attachment was like none other I have ever experienced. She was born at noon and by ten P.M. that night I was in a deep depression—feeling overwhelmed with protectiveness.

I (who am a fiercely independent person) went through similar periods throughout the next few months worrying about leaving her to return to work. Up until the birth of my son this past August, I was not able to shake this push-pull feeling.

When my son was born I felt a love for this second child, but also a separateness which I still haven't figured out. I love him, but I don't feel symbiotic with him! Since his birth I feel complete, stronger—an inner strength I never had before—as if his birth released me from a problem—that any crisis can be handled, because of the birth of this son. I didn't feel as bad returning to work—I realize I need to grow and develop in order to help my children grow and develop.

This Amazing New Person

I'm absorbed by your presence
—I watch . . . wait . . . almost
expecting you to disappear.
                              -Holly

Many parents describe a consistent reaction to their new babies: one of total captivation, with a surprising attunement to their babies' needs and perceptions. No matter how full the parents' lives had been before the arrival of this new person, nothing else seemed to command their attention and wonder quite like their newborns. Says Holly Piper:

> I was very awed by the whole birthing experience. For weeks after Emma was born I had the luxury of not really having to do anything but be with her. For a long time I felt like she was of another place—not at all grounded or aware of earthly existence. I felt an almost spiritual reverence about her. She really had me captivated—I'd watch her as she slept, trying to understand this little being and fearing she would disappear in a way if I took my eyes from her.

Women who have maintained a diversity of interests before parenthood may find being so completely absorbed in their new babies a surprising state of mind. Diane's story touches on the potential for conflict with previous goals and interests. "My career ambition," she says, "is to become a published writer and/or illustrator of children's books. I have a wide variety of interests and many hobbies—sometimes, I think, too many!" It was on the ride home from the hospital that Diane first noticed the change in herself:

> I felt very special and the world around me felt so mundane. It was such a neat feeling to be driving home with this little baby in the back seat. We were her parents! Not some other couple, but US!
>
> I wanted the present moment to go on and on and not change. Malori seemed so innocent and so perfect just the way she was. I realized I was appreciating the present time; I wasn't thinking about the past or planning the future. The "now" seemed too important. I wanted time to stand still for a while.

I didn't care about anything else but my new life with the baby. I realized this in full when my husband read a billboard announcing a new restaurant opening. Instead of piquing my interest, as it normally would, I felt total disinterest. I almost felt an intrusion on the mood when he mentioned we'd have to try it sometime.

I also felt like I'd never go back to any of my former interests. In fact, I even felt a little scared that I wouldn't ever want to pursue my interests in writing and illustrating children's books.

This total preoccupation only lasted days. As time went on, I became interested in my hobbies. But even now, four months later, I feel no strong urge to get back to writing. In fact, that is my latest struggle: wanting to "just" be a mother, doing hobbies in my spare time, vs. being a mother and pursuing another identity as writer/ illustrator.

From her experience of being "so caught up and aware of the present time," Diane retained "a heightened appreciation of savoring the moment." This has helped her, she says, in coping with the baby's fussy periods, and made her a more patient and confident person.

"I wish I had more time to be quiet and more alone with her," I wrote when my second child was two days old. "I'm so aware she's only a newborn for a few days, and nothing in this world is more luscious than a newborn baby. Heaven for me would be to be forever with my newborn in my arms—or else to see on everything the glow of the newborn . . ."

It isn't just our own child who can exert such powerful attraction; we can be captivated by the attractiveness in anyone or anything. Devi Novak, a teacher from the Ananda Community, described this magnetism in the course of a seminar on relationships:

I went to a Parents Training Seminar that Nitai gave, a wonderful experience, and we had to spend some time bonding with a child. The person I had to spend all morning with was Nalini, who is six years old. And I just fell in love with her. I couldn't take my eyes off her, she was so beautiful, so charming, and I felt utterly magnetically captivated by that little girl—and I still do.

And it was easy, because she was a little girl and I was a mother; but it's the same magnetism that you're attracted to in a man or a woman or a child or a chipmunk. There's something that's magnetically attractive about the creation. And sometimes it'll be in a member of the opposite sex, sometimes it'll be some beautiful part of nature.

But I looked into that little girl's face and I thought, "She is like a painting! She's the most exquisite thing I ever saw!" . . . And all of this world is God's wonderful magnetic thing.

The kind of bonding Devi describes can happen unexpectedly, almost by accident. In the following story, Anne's response to her granddaughter is very much like the absorption that new parents often feel.

Anne is forty–two, with grown children not much younger than herself from her husband's first marriage. "I really did not feel the need to have other children in my life," she says. "That all changed when my eleven–year-old granddaughter came to visit for the first time since she was six months old."

> When I looked at her, my eyes watered and I felt rather like I was watching myself watching myself. I saw my husband, our son, our daughter, my husband's mother and myself in her. She also said she felt she looked like me, and she knows I'm her stepgrandma and genetic tendencies do not apply to us. Yet I am she and she is I.
>
> I felt—alive (perhaps for the first time), trying to experience life as I think she sees it—that is, living entirely in the present, living on the edge. Practically everything took on an importance—oh, like puppies, trees, etc.—they weren't just there, they were real. I felt glorious, alive and vibrant, part of and connected to all of Life.
>
> All the while she was here, I seemed to be nudging myself to savor every minute because she would soon be gone. She totally consumed my world. I stared at her—whatever she did seemed miraculous. I didn't want to lose one minute being with her. I hardly slept more than a few hours a night. When she left after two weeks, I felt as if I'd lost my heart.

The time of total absorption in a new baby can be a delight. Janet is a woman who had long desired a child. Her relationship with her husband is "especially close," and her activities fit easily around a baby's presence. "Even before I was a mother," she says, "my days at home were never long enough. I like to cook, knit, read, write, make music, see friends. I love the challenge and scope of full-time homemaking. I am an optimist. My first clear word as a child was `yes.' I met the man of my dreams when I was just turned eighteen, and married him at twenty." Janet continues:

> That we would some day have children was always a given in our relationship. Both of us very much wanted them. We put it off the first three years because we wanted time alone together, and the second three years out of financial necessity. At long last I quit my job (wanting to be home full-time, but ready also to conceive), and was pregnant a month later.
>
> I have always loved the idea of being pregnant, and had looked forward to it eagerly. I also looked forward to labor and delivery as pinnacle emotional experiences. But how did I feel about the end product? I had had very little childcare experience as I grew up. I did not feel very drawn toward other people's newborns (in fact I would rather not hold them for fear of being left damp) and had very little

patience with others' toddlers. But I felt absolutely confident that I would be in love with my own baby.

From my journal:

And then he was out, and Dr. G. said, "It's a little Alexander!" She handed me my wet baby. I held him up in the air with my hands under his arms and around his chest. I just held him up and looked at him until Clifford said, "Put him on your chest, Honey." Then I held him close to me. I cut his cord. They left the three of us alone till the placenta came. I was in exquisite pain and joy! The cord was resting on my gaping fourth degree cut, and I couldn't wait to deliver the placenta. I would say how much I hurt, and Clifford would say, "Think about your baby."

I delivered the placenta a half hour after birth. Dr. G. sewed me up. It hurt a lot. I thought, "The pain is supposed to be over now!" But my baby was in my arms and that was all that mattered. And he was perfect.

I cried and cried on the phone to my sister: "We have a boy!!" What a wonder. He lay next to me, facing me; I gazed at him in awe, tenderly stroking the back of his soft, hairy head. He was perfectly beautiful. Lots of dark brown hair. Rosebud lips. Oh! And big!

I have never been so enervated. I nearly fainted the first few times that I walked. I was in tremendous pain, even with codeine. I had worked so long and hard with so little sleep and food. When I would lie down to try to sleep I couldn't because I was in too much pain. And my legs would feel like they were floating up and down in wave patterns below my knees! But we were too excited to sleep anyway!

We went home early the next morning to make room for another couple. I went to meet them, and told them my joy and what joy awaited them. At home, our boy's diaper was very dirty, and I changed it for the first time. I had so much fun doing it, and laughed a lot. He was so dirty and sticky and so miserable, scream-ing because he was naked. I ran around trying to figure everything out and managed to clean him up and get a fresh diaper on him.

Xander was cranky all night. I know now that I should have nursed him more than I did, but I was too exhausted and inexperi-enced to realize that.

Two days postpartum:

Clifford put on the McGarrigles' song "Bundle of Sorrow, Bundle of Joy." He was washing dishes. I cried when I heard the song, and came out and stood by him. We hugged and cried . . . Alexander does a thousand darling things that I wish I could capture and save forever. He shifted his eyes from side to side, slowly and repeatedly. I was amazed because it seemed a manifes-tation of intelligence.

Three days:
Clifford is amazed at my calmness with Alexander. He is much more frazzled when Xander is crying. I figure that I just can't let myself begin to be bothered; where would it end?

Six days:
Clifford went to work for the first time since Alexander was born. It was strange to call him there: me at home, him there, music playing in the background as usual. Everything the same, but everything different.

Nine days:
I spent the day just as I'm supposed to: resting, relaxing and enjoying my sweet baby. I love him so much, and tell him so over and over again.

Second week:
We got our first photographs back. Black and white. Beautiful. They brought back a flood of first days' emotions, and I cried to look at them. I love our little boy . . . I went out to a couple of stores, leaving Alexander for the first time (with Clifford). I felt very emotional, wanting to tell everyone I met that I have a two-week-old son whom I'm away from for the first time.

Third week:
Feeding Xander during the night is a pretty exhausting routine. I try to sleep with him during the day, but don't do it as much as I should. Lying next to my beautiful sleeping boy on the bed is still so new and wonderful that it's hard for me to fall asleep!

One month:
I'm crazy about my little boy. Even when he's screaming his head off in misery, I look at him in wonder and joy. He's so beautiful. The books say that often parents are disappointed with the real baby, in comparison with the dream baby that they had expected. But I could not have imagined a baby as wonderful as Alexander.

"My son is two years old tomorrow," Janet adds, "and has been delightful beyond my ability to imagine. He still breastfeeds; nursing him has been very precious to me.

"During the first few weeks of my son's life, I felt so close to him that at times I would feel like I was him. I would cry, and feel as if I were him crying. Stretching out my arms upon awakening, my mind would flash upon him doing the same thing, and I would feel as if he and I were one. It's precious to me to feel so linked to him."

Being so captivated, so in love with the baby makes it easier for a mother to put other interests aside and surrender to the baby's all-encompassing need for her. But the freedom to let oneself be so absorbed is not always available. Perhaps it can only happen with a first baby, a sensitive and generous partner, and no conflicting demands on the mother's attention.

~   ~   ~

"I felt instinctively attuned to his needs," says a new mother. Such attunement takes many parents by surprise. It seems to operate through several channels, including heightened sensory awareness, telepathy, empathy and synchronized body clocks. On the simplest level, mothers often find themselves tuned in to their baby's sleep and hunger cycles:

> I noticed that I would wake up to nurse my baby right before he woke up. When he was ready to eat I would be aware—with no let down reflex.
> I know when Molly is going to wake up from her naps; I'll be in the back yard and I'll know when to come in and it's always a few seconds before she wakes up, or she has woken up and she sits up and waits for me—it's like she knows I'm coming in.

As Susie Helme says, we "lose touch with linear time, as we wake and sleep with the baby. I think we even adapt our consciousness to theirs so that we wake when they need us (I remember I used to wake at 2 A.M., wide-eyed, and have the heat pad warm by the time Maya started snuffling for her feeding), so we plug suddenly into a more intuitive, primitive facet of our nature."

This awareness works even across greater distances, according to Anara Williams, who recalls:

> I had strong alarm systems all the time I was nursing; ie. knowing when the baby woke up or was about to even if I was out of the house, letting down when I was miles away exactly when he cried (my husband and I compared times), waking up before he did for night nursings. I think these are fairly commonplace experiences and they tapered off with weaning.

A nursing baby sets his mother's body rhythm to be ready with his next meal at the right time—but physical connections can't explain the experience of Joan, an adoptive mother. She writes:

> Our son arrived at age three months in March, 1985. Three days later I went out on some errands—the first time away from him since his arrival. Twice while I was out I heard a baby crying, but upon looking around for the baby, saw none.
> The next day I had a hairdresser's appointment. I heard a baby come in, crying, while the hairdresser was cutting. I mentioned to her about the baby and she informed me that no baby had just

arrived. But I heard it so distinctly! I began to catch on. I asked her what time it was. Upon arriving home I discovered that exactly at that time our son had awakened and begun to cry.

I have heard of the "imprinting" that takes place in those moments after the birth of a child, and I think this same imprinting process was at work in our case. I now feel that there is a great deal more that goes on during bonding than can be measured or observed, and that is not entirely a function of the birthing process itself.

Stories abound of parents sensing their child's need for them. A sudden impulse to check on the baby turns out to be surprisingly timely. Is it more than coincidence? Judy Farris describes an incident that happened three or four days after the birth of her son:

I had "limited rooming in" because of the caesarean but with nursing on demand. My private room was at the extreme opposite end of a long corridor from the nursery. I awoke at about 4:30 A.M. with a very strong urge to see my baby. I walked down to the nursery and noticed that Teddy was not in his bassinet. There he was, over the nurse's knee, screaming his lungs out while she was sticking his heel with a needle. Realizing what was going on, I knelt down beside him and tried to comfort him as best I could until the ordeal was over. Then I took him back to the room with me.

Judy adds that she felt bonded to this child all during her pregnancy, with surges of love whenever she felt him move.

Can we do anything to increase our attunement to the baby? Pam and Richard Myers felt that careful attention to their baby's environment, both before and after birth, helped to create an extraordinary connection. Pam says:

We prepared long and carefully for our first child's birth. I had paid close attention to diet and avoidance of alcohol, drugs, household chemicals and so forth during my pregnancy (as did my husband for the most part).

We had a short and harried hospital birth that drained much of our energies. We were glad to leave the hospital when we did, about four hours after our son's birth.

We were completely alone with our son for several hours before some good friends, who recognized the reverence due this new life, came by to pay their respects to the baby and the birthing family. For the most part, we consciously isolated ourselves from other people and stayed awake for a very long time (forty-eight hours?) after the birth to keep watch over our son and familiarize ourselves with the rhythms, appearance and habits of this new life.

We paid close attention to low lighting both for the birth and afterwards, to sound, and to what materials were coming in contact with his skin.

Our son seemed able to communicate his every need without words or motion. I felt that I knew his every thought and most of his feelings. This child remains to this day the best at nonverbal communication, and the most in tune with his parents' thoughts and feelings, and understanding of our actions.

It was the first time I felt no need whatsoever for words with another human being, with the exception of a couple of experiences during lovemaking. It was the beginning of my realization of how sexual and sensual an experience birthing is.

Like Pam, Robin Kristufek was paying attention to her first baby even before his birth. She had experienced years of infertility and had been wanting a child for a long time:

I went through a long spiritual, emotional and medical (herbal and acupuncture treatment) process to finally achieve pregnancy. So, I was well prepared on many levels—there was a well-prepared place in my life for the baby. He was very welcomed in our lives.

Of course during labor one feels altered . . . To me labor was just the beginning, the spark of it all. It turned my focus inward, to my body, and the incredible forces coming through it. I felt as if my body was a channel, that energy was pouring one hundred miles an hour in through the top of my head, down and out my vagina and down my legs. I think having no numbing drugs and allowing yourself to feel this energy helps to open you up to more unusual energies.

After birth, the focus goes all onto the baby. It seemed like the whole world (really my whole focus) shifted: from myself to another small one outside. Every moment feeling in tune, vibrating with him like with no other person before. I knew and felt what he wanted and felt, more than I had ever experienced with anyone before. This is a very intense experience. It's like telepathic communication, or energy exchange between two people, incredibly strong.

A few hours after her daughter's birth, Gail and her husband both felt a change in their awareness. She suggests it was caused by shifting into a mind frame of attunement:

The fog was very thick that morning and it was raining periodically. John had to go home around eleven for some clothes and the car seat. He got home and forgot why he was there! He called me and got oriented.

Only nine hours after the birth, we were driving home. This is when the altered awareness occurred most for me, but also for John. We both commented on how everything seemed to be in slow motion. The car felt like it was floating. I had a slight case of shivers (let me mention that no drugs were used in the delivery—it was totally natural). The baby was so tiny that the car seemed bigger than usual. Everything about our world seemed different. Like I was an alien from another planet. I think I was beginning to connect with Laurel and her perceptions and feelings, so that I could respond to her accurately. The altered awareness came from trying to leave one mind frame—one person, independent, mentally one individual—for a new mind frame which gave priority to a stranger who could not express herself, so it was my job to read this new life.

Beyond awareness of the baby's needs, many parents believe they feel his feelings and share in his perceptions. "The first unusual thing I noticed," says Linda Wyatt, "was a feeling of `connectedness' with my baby. I hadn't expected this. I couldn't understand how people could let their baby cry—it was impossible for me because when he cried, I could feel it. It was like I was feeling what he was feeling—frustration, anger, and so on."

At times, these sensations intensify into a vivid moment of identification with the newborn. "My experience was quite brief," says Joyce, "but something I'll never forget. Caitlyn was born on the fourth of September. I believe it was either the fifth or sixth when I had what I now call my `symbiosis' experience."

I was lying on our bed—Caitlyn was sleeping nearby. The sun was shining onto the bed. I remember being frozen in the moment—feeling "out-of-body" for a moment as I looked at my hands; and it was as if I was looking at a newborn's hands. I felt like I was a newborn. I was caught by the length of my fingernails as they seemed too long (I later cut them very short).

Everything looked unusually bright. The sun was shining in the window—but it was as if everything was illuminated. I just lay there for what seemed a long period of time caught in this moment where I was a newborn. I felt very warm and peaceful. My breathing also felt like I was a newborn baby—hard to explain. It was as if I could feel each breath in my chest. I'm not sure I had ever felt that peaceful before—completely relaxed—body, mind, spirit. I believe it was Caitlyn's stirrings which brought me back to reality.

When it ended, I felt at first peaceful, then kind of scared. I thought I was "losing my mind." I asked my midwife about it and he said, "Oh yes, that's normal"—but I've never heard anyone else say anything about it or even similar.

Though Joyce had never heard of anything like this, first-time mothers seem to be particularly prone to such feelings. However, people differ in their reactions to the experience of feeling like a newborn themselves. Some women find it adds to the closeness and helps them to be comfortable with the baby. "I felt so peaceful and calm," said Joyce, "that I assumed Caitlyn also felt the same way—which made me feel pleased."

Janet sometimes felt as though she and her baby were one. She took the experience to mean that she was very close to her son, and says, "If it had any effect on our relationship, it was to make me feel even closer to him."

In contrast, some mothers who have moments of feeling like a newborn judge them to be an escape from the reality of motherhood. Marisa writes:

> About two weeks after my son was born, I was lying in bed and began to feel like an infant. I saw and felt myself begin to move like one, to see like one, to make infant sounds; I felt glassy-eyed as an infant often looks. It was as though I were a baby in the bed.
>
> It felt good—I almost felt like staying there. I began to flow with it because it felt so warm and secure—but there always seemed to be a part that observed and wouldn't let me slip into it.
>
> I had been basically a "flower child" and then deserted by my husband because he wanted to "be free" and I was living in my parents' very conservative home—so a regression state like this makes perfect psychological sense.
>
> It happened two or three times at the same time of day when my son was asleep in the crib across the room, and then stopped as I had to face reality and be a Mother! Which, by the way, I love, and have always absolutely adored my son, though I didn't want him particularly before birth.
>
> Maybe it was my mind's way of trying to escape the sadness of the situation I was in at the time. I wouldn't suggest regression of this nature to anyone at any time, because it is not reality, but escape—even though it was not unpleasant.

There are moments when one almost seems to be seeing through the baby's eyes. Bunny Chidester describes her experiences with her firstborn son, when he was around two weeks old:

> It was mainly a feeling that I was the baby. Sometimes when we'd be lying in bed nursing, I could tune in to him and center on him and I would see the room and our surroundings through his eyes. Everything looked so BIG!
>
> I could also feel his total contentment and positive vibes flowing from him toward me and back. My body felt like he must have felt: small, vulnerable, yet happy and content. It even got to the point that when I'd wake up in the morning I'd marvel at how big my

husband's face looked to me, and even my own face in the bathroom mirror!

I enjoyed it, but found it quite strange. So much so that I didn't tell anyone about my feelings. I felt it was maybe from my caring for him so much, and his being so small that all else was looking so big.

Anara Williams has two sons, and with each birth she experienced a mysterious shift of perception. She believes she was actually "seeing through the infant's eyes":

After each child was delivered, there was a time of waiting for the placenta to deliver. Each time, the new baby was given to the same trusted friend to hold. While she stood holding the bundled baby and I lay on the bed trying to concentrate on pushing out the placenta, the same vision appeared.

I don't know if my eyes were open or shut but I saw myself, lying on the bed naked, hair wet and clinging to my face. Each time the view was from the point in the room where the baby was. And although I need glasses to see farther than four or five feet in front of me, when I "saw" myself from across the room, the focus was perfect.

At the second birth the baby was out of the room and I did not see myself until Beth came and stood in the doorway holding him. And when the placenta was delivered (in the first case) the vision disappeared. (In the second birth I could not deliver the placenta, began hemorrhaging, and things got pretty fuzzy after that.)

I believe this was possible because the baby and I were still attached, despite the cord being cut. Yes, I did feel that I was seeing myself through the infant's eyes—or rather I knew it to be so. At the time I didn't even question what I experienced, only later did I realize: oh, so that's what it was.

It reminds me of that whole subterranean, unseen intuitive life that is easily forgotten or overlooked in the daily hubbub. I think of those bonding times and am reassured that there is sense and rhythm to this parenting business—and to life as a whole.

~ ~ ~

Parents tend to perceive special qualities in their babies. "We all think our own geese are swans"—but perhaps loving eyes can see things that would escape an "objective" observer. Nancy, for example, saw remarkable intelligence in her baby:

In the early months after I had Brenden I would look at him at times and know he was attempting communication with me through his eyes. Though I knew this was happening, I was unable (blocked somehow) to participate in his attempts to communicate. Something was haywire in me, and still is. This caused great frustration in Brenden and he would cry miserably.

I would do whatever I could, knowing that I could not remove my "block" and also knowing we would have to suffer through this "short-circuit" together. I wanted him to know that, though I was unable to do what he needed, I still cared. I believe he eventually understood this, but I know also that my inability was his loss, as well as my own.

Many parents perceive their baby as wise and knowing. Is it because newborns are so impressive in their wordless intelligence? Is it because at some point they typically look like Buddhas—serious, calm, round-bellied and round-headed, the bridge of the nose still rather flat, the cheeks broad . . . Or have these parents seen something real, as they look with unguarded eyes?

Describing her newborn, Helen says, "When they brought him in and laid him next to me, I looked in his eyes and experienced an insight that has never left me. 'The Wisdom of the Ages' was there."

Robin Kristufek's impressions of her firstborn son were similar:

Kyle seemed fluid, all-knowing and eternally wise somehow. And I connected with that for that brief time. Adults and even other children older than Kyle seemed grossly large, not smooth, with energy blocks up the yinyang. Kyle seemed so pure and just right. Flowing more.

A climax came on day two or three, as we both sat and watched the sunset. It was a vibrant, brilliant orange. Kyle watched it for a solid five or more minutes, his lips pursed in wonder. He was enraptured by it. I felt that he was remembering, rediscovering. To watch him see this for the first time (again?) was overwhelming.

Trina Simon describes her impressions of her newborn daughter:

I've previously had feelings of being in "history," of past lives. When the baby and I went home, she was going through facial and even hand movements and changes that I could see were *her* past lives—I saw her as a Chinese monk, for example.

I felt a total fascination with the baby's face, feelings, and so on. A few weeks later, she would seem to be watching some type of spiritual entity. She always watched it at the same spot and her face would go through all these expressions . . .

Some parents perceive their baby as being old. Anita, for example, while suffering from postpartum depression saw her baby girl as an old, sad woman. Donna Kurtz recalls that when she first held and looked at her second child, "I knew he was really a very old man staring out of that infant face. We stared intently at each other for some time and I whispered to him, `Okay, old man, it's time to be a baby now.' And he did become an infant, although he's never really been a baby—in looks or demeanor." *

Parents sometimes have a strong impression that the newborn has traveled here from another realm. Therese describes her newborn daughter: "She struck me as a comet that had come whirling through space on to my bed, between my legs."

"When my baby first came out," Trina Simon recalls, "she looked around at everyone in the room, as though in awe of the whole experience—and my feeling was that she had come from very far away, very quickly—that she was just as `blown away' by it all as we were."

~ ~ ~

The most mysterious of these early impressions may be the sense of recognizing our newborn. Yet it seems to happen fairly often. "I loved the baby and wanted him and was surprised by how much I felt like I knew him," says Linette. "We were old friends already Owen and I."

---

*Parents may not be aware that some newborns do in fact have an "old" appearance, for phsical reasons. Occasionally, towards the end of a normal pregnancy the placenta becomes inadequate, leading to problems and special needs in the newborn. These are described in *The Earliest Relationship* (Addison-Wesley,1990) by Brazelton and Cramer:

> Chris was a long, lean baby when born at forty-one weeks, one week overdue . . . Weighing six pounds, three ounces, he looked like a famine victim. His skin was loose, peeling on his hands and feet and a bit on his belly. His hair was fine and rather sparse. But the most striking thing about his appearance was his old-man face with a very worried look. As he lay in his crib, his eyes were wide open, staring anxiously off into the room . . . When he was moved even slightly, his face wrinkled up into a frightened animal-looking expression, and he let out a piercing, high-pitched wail . . . The medical team . . . explained to his mother that he was a typical dysmature baby with low fat and sugar stores. Due to no fault of hers, her placenta had "given out" and had not served him at the end of her pregnancy. Hence, he'd probably lost weight in the past three weeks . . . The intrauterine stress {leads} to poor energy stores and hypoglycemia, coupled with other probably endocrine imbalances. These in turn lead to a kind of hypersensitivity to sensory stimuli . . . Every response is painful to these babies and creates a painful reaction in the parents around them.

It can be very hard for parents to feel close to these babies. Brazelton and Cramer offer suggestions for easing the adjustment while the baby's metabolism gradually rights itself.

Therese describes her first view of her daughter as she was born into her husband's hands: "I saw *all* of her, all of her life, all of her soul, I could see her from beginning to end and back again, I knew her instantly, totally."

Colleen Waddell's response to her first child seemed to her an extension of what she had felt during pregnancy:

> ... a feeling that I "already had children." When my son was born, though he was a "stranger," we knew each other beyond this normal awareness. It seemed eternal. I felt he had always been with me. It seems that about five days postpartum this peaked and then slowly diminished.

Since the concept of bonding has become well-known, many parents have grieved for lost opportunities to make the deepest possible contact with their baby at birth. The story of Sarah Laird involves a mother who not only was unconscious during the delivery, but was unable to see her child until the following day. It offers a counterbalance to the fear that a connection must be made immediately, or we'll become unavailable to love.

> I'm forty-two years old now and ten years ago I gave birth to my first and only child, Mary Dana. I'd like to tell you the whole story of how I met my husband and how I knew within about three hours that he was my "soul-mate" and that we would definitely marry, but that is another "altered awareness" story. We married when I was almost thirty years old and had already established myself in my career.
>
> I knew immediately that I had conceived and that my child was conceived in love. I remember the feeling and the certainty and the awe and wonder of it so well. The connectedness that I will describe next really began at the moment of conception.
>
> My pregnancy was normal until eight weeks before my due date, at which time I began hemorrhaging and spent the rest of the time in bed. Slightly before my due date my doctor induced labor and Mary Dana was born at about 10:30 P.M.
>
> I was under heavy sedation and was completely unaware of her delivery. Not only was I unaware, but I was given up for dead by the anesthesiologist after I began hemorrhaging profusely at delivery and my blood would not clot. My obstetrician kept working on me in spite of the fact that I had no vital signs, and somehow I made it through the crisis and lived.
>
> I woke up in the middle of the night with quite a few worried looking doctor faces peering down at me. They gave me a guarded explanation of what had happened and told me I had a girl. I felt nothing upon hearing this, except, perhaps, a slight disappointment that it hadn't been a boy. Mostly I was out of sorts. I noticed that

my stomach had gone down but I felt absolutely nothing maternally.

For several hours, perhaps until about mid-morning, they would not bring my baby to me, although my husband had seen her. This was because I was running a fever and they didn't want to endanger her. I was petulant about this, quite honestly because I was just bored and felt that, after going through all that misery, I should at least get a look at my baby. Finally they brought her to me.

Bob, my husband, was in the room with me. He says he will never forget the look on both of our faces when we saw each other for the first time. He says we were locked in a gaze that was so strong, so committed.

I remember feeling that I was seeing someone I knew already in the most intimate and personal way. It was like a reunion, and from that moment on I was "in love" with her in the deepest sense. I really do compare it to meeting my husband . . . a recognition of a soul mate.

It has made my relationship with my baby (and little girl, as she has grown) the most committed one I can imagine. Motherhood seems to me now to be a special state of grace.

Do such impressions come only to parents who believe they may have been with their children in another existence? Judith Skutch is well known today as the publisher of *A Course In Miracles*. But she was a fairly conventional young mother in 1959, when her second child was born. Though she was awake during delivery, the moment she describes in her book *Double Vision* (Celestial Arts, 1985) came a few hours later:

I was awakened gently from a deep and forgetful sleep. "Do you want to hold your little girl?" I held out my arms to my new daughter and the nurse left us alone . . . And then I looked down at her, peacefully breathing by my heart, for the first time.

In that instant I felt a shock of recognition so strong I nearly dropped my child. It reverberated through my body in jolts and I trembled violently. Tears poured down my cheeks as I sobbed aloud "Thank God, you're here. At last you're here." I did not know, intellectually, what I meant. I experienced only awareness of profound relief, as if a sigh long held were just released. An unrecognized tension gave way to a mighty joy. I felt propelled into an ecstasy I could not measure, andwave after wave of gratitude engulfed me. "You're finally here," I repeated, as if to a much-missed friend.

Part II

A DIARY
OF
NEWBORN TIME

3

My Story

*P*eople may hesitate to speak of their experiences during the newborn year, fearing that others will judge them "not normal." So they keep silent and wonder about themselves—as I wondered about the changes I noticed after my son's birth.

In the midst of an experience that amazed me, I found it impossible even to hint at what I was going through. My husband, Nicholas, was the only person to whom I dared reveal something of what I was feeling and sensing. But I entrusted my observations to the pages of my diary. Written while I was immersed in the experience, they convey its essence more truly than a later reminiscence ever can.

To understand the impact of these experiences, it's helpful to know something of my earlier life. Since I was young, a mystery has led me on. It's the age-old puzzle of body and mind: which is which? And what are we? Many of my ventures have been along paths I hoped would lead to an answer.

At thirteen, I first encountered the moods of adolescence. I'd never known sleepless nights, day-long irritability and inexplicable anger; suddenly, all these were part of my life. I assumed "the curse" and its mysterious hormones were to blame, and I resented it. Meanwhile, Mother was enduring the rather similar discomforts of menopause. I remember her exasperated comment, "It's as if nature tries to get rid of you, once you're no longer useful!"

I resented what seemed the indignity of being a woman. I wanted to be free of this interference with my state of mind. How could I trust my emotions if they were controlled by hormones, those biological storm-troopers? How could I know what was myself and what was chemistry? So I fumed, stabbed diary pages with damns, hurled my eraser at the wall . . . and gradually got used to the new circumstances.

But I couldn't conclude that we are just faulty animals—not after a ghostly kiss startled me awake one morning. I didn't know it at the moment, but my grandmother had died the day before, five thousand miles away. The puzzle became more complex: mind, body and spirit. How could these pieces fit and make sense together, each seeming to belong to a different dimension and to go by different rules?

A few years later, I read about the "Good Friday experiment." Volunteers were given a psychedelic drug; spending hours in a chapel and listening to sacred music, many had mystical experiences. Psychedelic states were new territory in those days, and it was shocking to think spiritual revelations could depend on altered chemistry.

Effects of mind on body, and of body on mind—these were the most interesting questions I could imagine. I've been asking them ever since in various ways. I studied psychology, nursing and yoga, surmised wonderful insights waiting in the fields of neurology, parapsychology and biofeedback, but always grew discouraged before the huge and ever-increasing mass of facts to be encompassed.

What I really wanted to touch was closer to home, an experience that might retreat from an intellectual grasp. I wanted to step outside the confines of my habitual mind, and meet the world in a fresh and innocent way. With a psychedelic, I once entered another level of perception, sensing enormous friendly life in all objects around me. Lifting a glass of water to my lips, I felt the universe tip it for me, its child. The air was full of silver webs. I ran my fingers through the air and wondered, "If there's no such thing as spirit, what is all this stuff?"

Meditation helped me sometimes to find stillness, but life went on in its contradictory way, and at twenty-two I decided to re-experience the psychedelic shift. I hoped it would help me cut through emotional tangles and discover a path forward. Nothing happened. But apparently the drug, although it seemed to make no impression, had dissolved some inner boundary. Over the following weeks I was energized, elated and finally swamped by fantasies and lovely vision, sense of revelation and wild misreading of events. For a while, I was crazy. My familiar self, scattered like a reflection in water, came slowly back together.

Since then, I respect the powers of my own mind, and I no longer trust it very far. I know some of its delusions and subconscious story-lines, and how skillfully it projects them on the world.

~   ~   ~

And here I was at thirty-two expecting my first child, and wondering if I could really be fond of a baby. "I don't want to become an extension of my child," I worried in the last week. "At least I want to notice the tendency to make myself different because of the new role—as if I had to paint my thoughts in pastel colors now. Even for myself. As if even my thoughts must all be fresh and ready to be put on view! I do not want to be deprived of my own self just because I am becoming a mother."

Ten years had gone by since my journey through that other state, but I still had my mental map of the territory. I never guessed how useful it would become, shortly after my son's birth on February 13, 1980. The diary begins two days later . . .

~   ~   ~

Our baby boy was born just forty-nine hours ago. I had an unusually hard birth and needed help from forceps. Baby's shoulders and head were both of big circumference and my pushing was not bringing him down the birth canal. So I experienced the actual birth as a violent and traumatic one and yet the baby is perfect and unharmed in any way we can detect.

He is beautiful and absorbing. How few things in life make us smile irresistibly! I feel as if I live in a new world or as if new eyes and ears have been given to me. "Behold, I make all things new." My little teacher has already taught me the depth of my fear, and taught me to let go of some of my pride, in having to admit I needed help—and not to judge others as weak in a situation I haven't experienced. Hope I don't forget too soon.

He spent his first night mostly in my arms while Nicholas had a well-deserved sleep. I couldn't stop looking at his face.

> *The feel of your skin has entered my fingers,*
> *the softness of your newborn face*
> *is part of me forever.*
> *And every little sound you make is written in my skin . . .*

In the morning his father came and we spent the day looking at our son and holding him and talking about him and ourselves, until it was time for us to go home. All day February 13 it had snowed and the world was white.

Today, I needed to rest, so we didn't let anybody come to visit. Nearly all day long Young Son was sleeping. He wasn't even interested in nursing very much. We kept asking each other, "What shall we name him?" We kept smiling at each other, and the house was full of love and sunshine. Nick says, "The happiness he has brought with him into this house is unmeasurable." This parenthood makes you stupid, he says, because all your head goes to your heart.

Third day

These first few days are so precious—I remind myself now not to cling to the special bliss of these days with their incredibly heightened sensitivity to beauty and love. It is sometimes like swimming or floating in a sea of bliss—like feeling the presence of God in the house as a rosy aura of love and a deep soft breathing.

"Don't you see, God's grace is always flowing down." So is love, God and bliss all the same element and all pervading.

I long for the milk to come in, Devin is growing impatient with his hunger.

It's almost impossible to interest myself in any subject other than our baby . . . well, parenthood in general. To talk with people on other subjects is quickly fatiguing. All my energy flows to the experiencing of love and bliss with Devin and Nicholas and yes, even Rose the cat. I feel a new bond with my parents, especially Father, in now having a son. Dreams this morning revealed how important it is to me to complete the trinity of father-husband-son.

Fourth day

My milk came in early this morning in a gradual way so that I scarcely realized it was happening until I saw it oozing around Devin's little mouth as he nursed. I had been hearing the swallowing sounds and thinking they were something wrong! What a joy to be able to satisfy my little baby. Now he can be awake and calm, looking around with his beautiful eyes. He seems to be soothed by music.

Yesterday evening as I lay resting in bed drifting near sleep, I had a thought about Devin being ill or in an accident and at once felt a strange warm flush all over even to the fingertips as if plunged in warm water. Again the sensation came to various other thoughts about him (hearing/seeing his name called/written in the dark). I should have guessed it was the beginning of the milk. This morning I had an intense nightmare of Nick falling unconscious with the baby in his arms—myself running into the room, pulling Nick away from the heater he'd fallen against, shaking him and feeling for a pulse and screaming Oh God, Oh God, waking then with the same hot flush tingling all through me . . .

Fifth day

During the night my milk came in much more fully. First I noticed that my heart was beating away at 108 a minute as I lay in bed. Then I became warm and sweaty all over. Suddenly my breasts outgrew my nursing bra and began to throb!

Before that, as I was just lying feeling hot, I felt my "shakti*" is aroused. I even had thoughts of anxiety about it. I found it best to substitute a mantra** for thoughts, all of which seemed to make me

---

*Shakti: An Indian term denoting a latent energy in the body.
**Mantra: A word or phrase repeated for its calming or centering effect.

even more stimulated. But it is clear that this process is such an opening—is this the way for women? I used to want a "kitestring" and thought it would be provided by a husband but perhaps the real kitestring is Devin—something that makes you stay grounded because you must take care of it, so that you can safely fly high. I can't say it's just hormones. I know it's love, God's presence, grace.

Sixth day

It's silly I suppose but in the midst of my happiness in Devin I am always feeling how dreadfully fast these precious days are flying. If only we could have him for one year just as wonderful as he is right now! To know that he is "changing and developing every hour" makes me sad! Already my baby newborn is almost a week old!

Funny hallucination I keep having—seeing my hands as his hands—so tiny and soft. My whole body at times I sense as tiny like Devin. Even Nicholas looks tiny . . . tiny face . . . all is so sweet. Our cat looks full of love and intelligence. She seems to be enjoying the love in the air. Our house is so beautiful to me. The walls that once looked white now appear rosy and blue! And every silvery surface looks soft and liquid.

Had my first "negative" thought about Devin and felt so bad about it. I looked at him and he didn't look beautiful—his cheeks seemed too fat and low-slung and he has a double chin! I got depressed thinking it's so important to me for him to be beautiful, thinking my love for him could diminish if he doesn't look pretty. Then I felt so awful that his newborn days are gone already and that precious first face has disappeared.

It has been a day of such intense emotion for me. This morning I got shaky after a bath and was really forced to lie down nearly all day. It was a springlike day with a blue and white sky. Talking with Nicholas about Devin's birth, I was able at last to cry about it—the sadness that I gave him such a hard and violent start in life, regret that I could not do more to help him, then I suddenly could remember the feeling of the doctor trying with the forceps to bring his head down; I could feel again the hardness of bone against bone, unyieldingness of my body, simply the brutality of it, like forcefully rattling a key in a lock it doesn't fit. It was a great relief to cry that one out of the deep place where I'd hidden it these past five days. With Nick's love to comfort me and Devin in my arms it was simultaneously bliss and sadness, and felt like a really necessary cleansing.

Nick's eyes are so glistening and the bond between us is like an umbilical cord of light and warmth. The intensity of these experiences at times seems almost too much to bear.

Seventh day

Awoke with the feeling I've reconciled myself to the quick passing of time. Devin has come into my life like a wave of joy. You can't cling to a wave as a thing, but meet it and flow with it as a process. Devin jams us into the here and now, for his changes are quicker than we can keep up with. We can't predict anything about him from what happened four hours ago, or yesterday. He forces us to pay total attention.

The particle board on my cabinet next to my head in bed is just random splotches. It is full of hundreds of baby faces in all possible expressions!—and absolutely nothing else. The branches of the tree outside my window create baby faces with their patterns. Even the letters of the words as I write turn unexpectedly into baby faces. So it seems I'm always looking at the form of this Guru-Devin who has come to me. God has given me at last a form I could "see everywhere." If I were experiencing all this without Nicholas and Devin here, I don't doubt I would be in the state you know of.

My biggest mistake in the past week was not limiting visitors' time with us. Now, I can't believe what long and complex and strained visits I tolerated earlier in the week. It is clear now that I can't bear the strain of visits longer than a few minutes with most people.

We thought that Nick could go to work at least a few hours by tomorrow but now it seems I have far less stamina than before. I become trembly and am literally forced to lie down and go into blissyness. Is it Devin who is forcing me to create the calm he needs? I am eager to do so many things—I long to be up and cleaning and polishing Devin's house . . . but I am forced to lie still and learn to flow.

Eighth day

As you wash them,
take time to love
the glasses and the spoons.

I guess it's no accident that baby things are pink and blue. It must be because when your bambooni gets you high you see pink and blue all over everyplace! Do you suppose the baby's aura is sky blue and mine is rosy, and therefore pink, blue and lilac are all over?

Since obviously (apparently) what you see "out there" is what you are "in here," if Nick's eyes since late last night look less glowy and more guarded, less wide open and more shadow-curtained, how do I know whether I am seeing my own idea of him, or perceiving his tiredness, his distress at trying to divide himself into father and businessman, his frustration at the vast amount of work to be done and the lack of time? Do I simply ask—or open myself up and pay attention and let him flow into me instead of intruding myself into him. And if his vibration seems jangly, how do I know whether I'm feeling his state, or my own? It seems one must be careful not to put too much blind faith in one's perceptions, but find a way to be quiet and tune in with the heart and mind.

How cute—the spout of the teapot appears to be "sucky"!

Ninth day

When compassion comes, the heart finds relief from its loneliness.

Tenth day

As yogis gaze upon a candleflame, nursing mothers practice gazing on their babies. And because the baby's head rests on their heart, they practice meditation on the heart center . . .

Nick in his sleep is patting the spot on his chest where Devin's head would be, and murmuring to him. (Devin himself is sleeping under the covers between my legs.)

The key to Devin's behavior at this moment seems to be a matter of rhythm. Sudden changes of rhythm seem to be hard on him. It is we who assume he'll hate his diaper changes and therefore hurry our actions as fast as we can, thus losing touch with the little person there before us, who has been linked with my rhythm or Nick's rhythm in an intimate dance and now is suddenly jarred by our nervous haste and dread of his cries. I changed his diaper a while ago and because I was very tired was moving very slowly. Rather than becoming upset as he often does, he remained calm and alert even though he was exposed to the cool air for much longer than usual. Thus he continues to demolish all my notions one after another. I have only to make a statement about him for him to contradict it in the next moment.

Let the Right Brain take care of the infant child.

When I find myself hurrying or tensing to the point that my abdomen has tightened and I am holding my breath, it helps to repeat as a mantra "Be patient" and harmonize my breathing to it. Devin is teaching us all we need to know to care for him.

Be patient . . .

And cease to struggle in the arms of God.

Two weeks

Silver ringing tone in right ear. Spontaneous movements in legs and feet during relaxed resting . . . sleep for half an hour at a time then must be active. Cobwebs everywhere when Father here— silver eyelashes on Father. Drops of silver, visible as streaks of falling heavy light like mercury . . . I feel them on me like warm drops of breastmilk.

> . . . *all the people you have hurt*
> *because your heart would not hold them*
> *because they were too much like you . . .*

Three weeks

Fortunately, most of the intense effects are over now, leaving me with eyes and heart open—but not so much that I don't have to work at it.

~   ~   ~

> *Is it possible that birth, and the*
> *physical-chemical changes it induces,*
> *can open us, or make us able to*
> *perceive a different level of reality?*
> *- Nancy*

My diary of those weeks following Devin's birth records mostly my joyful surprise; it doesn't reveal how close I was to being manic and delusional. But even at the time, I was aware of it. When I spent most of every night awake and wandering around the house on one errand or another, I remembered the total sleeplessness of insanity. When my favorite picture of a saint began to stream "holy ash" that vanished at a closer look, I knew I was entering the realm of inside-out perception that I call "hallucinating freely." And when my thoughts revolved exciting theories of my baby as Saint Francis reborn, I recognized the pattern and the feeling of spiraling fantasy.

What kept me sane was a combination of luck and knowledge. Because I was familiar with the approach to a manic state, I could pull back when I got too close. I could stop my racing thoughts by replacing them with a quieting phrase. But it was luck that kept me resting on the couch instead of carrying out overblown plans—my body was just too weak. I was lucky to have a husband who shared my joy but not my fantasies, and a doctor who didn't over-react when Nick worried about my lack of sleep.

Even then, I knew this was a strange combination of heavenly bliss and mental malfunction. A thoroughly positive state, I thought, would not include the sensory slip-ups, nor the intolerance I sometimes felt toward Nick. I wondered how to value such a mix. Was I normal? Was I crazy? When everything glowed with tender beauty, was I seeing the world's real face—or just the effects of a private intoxication?

As I've tried to understand my own and other people's stories, I've discovered how hard it is to separate the facts of an experience from our interpretation of them. We tell our story according to our beliefs, selecting and arranging the events of our lives to fit a pattern of which we may be only half aware.

Like most people, I hold different and conflicting beliefs at the same time. When Devin was born, I was a student of yoga, and I thought in terms of kundalini (or shakti, as it's also called)—a latent energy "sleeping" at the base of the spine. It seemed the intense pressure of birth must have aroused that energy. But then, I wondered, why doesn't this happen to every woman who goes through a difficult delivery?

As a nurse, I thought about the effects of prolactin and other hormones, though I'd never heard they could cause such radical changes of perception. And I wondered whether my altered awareness could be part of a spiritual awakening, a bit of grace that I needed to open my heart to my baby.

Several people have offered explanations of what I experienced. One man diagnoses "psycho-physiologic imbalance." Another suggests that my heart chakra was opened fully. "In the terminology of the Caballa," he says, "the Nechzach Sephiroth was activated." A mother writes:

> The combination of being not quite enthusiastic about becoming a parent, and the difficult birth, was the reason why you experienced the heightened sense of love and tenderness. Your "higher self" knew that an extended experience such as yours was needed to bring you closer to your baby. Your creative or spiritual side was expressing itself.

Another woman raises an important question:

> Your perceptions of color changes and of aluminum appearing "soft" sounded strange to me. I can't understand why these changes in perception would accompany the post-natal feelings. My question is this: Has there been anyone who answered your questionnaire who has never used any form of mind-altering

drug, who reported experiences similar to yours? I wonder if, somehow, the chemical changes induced by birth triggered something of a "flashback" for you.

Among the people who shared their stories with me, about thirty stated they have never taken any psychedelics. They describe every kind of experience in newborn time, with one exception: None noticed any great degree of sensory heightening. They tended rather to have psychic, visionary and emotional experiences. So there may be a link between intensified sensory awareness and previous use of psychedelics. But which is cause and which is effect? Do mind-altering drugs perhaps sensitize us to some of our own hormones, altering our normal response?

Once I hoped it would be possible to say, "This is illusory, that is real . . . This is my body, with all its effects on my awareness, and this is *me*." But it seems there are no such clear boundaries, and this is never more evident than during the newborn year, when all boundaries are in flux.

Part III

I AM CHANGED

All my boundaries are in flux
with unpredictable results—
my focus, my way of sensing time,
of feeling and moving my own body,

inner boundaries of dreams and waking,
boundaries of myself and others
myself and my baby
myself and the world—all shifting, permeable . . .

I'm open to presences,
emotion, memories,
my senses are opened—
I know that I am changed.

4

A Changing Body & Altered Senses

I've always noticed women seem changed
after giving birth: more conscious,
slowed down, a different tone in their
voices, more sensitive.
- Linda

*A*fter childbirth, a woman's body may feel different and move in new ways—not only because it is physically altered, but because it reflects her changing awareness. She may expect to feel drained after labor, and many do speak of exhaustion: "TIRED ... Would I ever rest enough?" "I have never been so enervated..." She may experience unfamiliar weakness. (I remember the astonishing sensation of being too weak to rise on tiptoes—after having taught strenuous yoga classes into my seventh month of pregnancy!) Lightheaded and dizzy and prone to faint when climbing out of a hot bath— none of this is surprising considering the blood loss and other stresses of childbirth.

Yet there is often a feeling of new energy, even along with physical depletion. Mothers often mention their surprise at long hours of wakefulness right after delivery: "My water broke at 1:30 on a Thursday morning, I had my baby at 2:03 Friday morning and I finally slept Sunday night—meanwhile I was too thrilled and too happy to sleep." Others recall:

> I remember, immediately following the birth, how exhilarating it was. I had so much energy I couldn't sleep! I finally wound down eighteen hours after the birth. She was born at five A.M.; I had previously been up since ten A.M. the morning before! A total of thirty-seven hours.

> Noah was born at midnight and I was put to bed after recovery and spent the night wide awake with boundless energy and God-praising thoughts running through my head.

This wakefulness, like the shaking that sometimes follows delivery, is probably based in the body's chemistry. Perhaps it is a way of absorbing or releasing the energies of birth. A midwife says, "I find when I go to a laboring woman's home, or enter the room where she is, I often get the shakes as if in an effort to integrate the powerful energy there."

Initial wakefulness can last longer and become a new pattern. In mental and emotional illness after childbirth, it becomes a serious, persistent inability to sleep. But for many women, wakefulness seems to be part of a heightened energy that eases the early days and nights of mothering. Even an adoptive mother, Patricia, noticed "much less sleep required."

"Although my body was actually weaker," Linda says, "I felt somehow energized. I could feel the energy flow in my body. I was too awake to nap in the daytime very much. At night I was sleeping about two and a half hours at a time—waking to nurse and change the baby. Didn't feel tired at all, even in the morning."

Therese recalls, "After my second baby was born I was `shot from guns' filled with energy, needed little sleep for three months; this gradually tapered down and now I'm somewhat back to normal but almost couldn't sleep after birth!"

The body may even feel renewed. At forty-one, seven months after her child was born, actress Goldie Hawn described this beautifully:

> I feel reborn since the baby. I feel fifteen. It's something that's almost chemical. I feel that all the organs and parts of my body have been electrified, and they're all sort of shining and glimmering. Like my machine is new. Yes, I'm tired in the morning and so on, but my spirit isn't like that—my spirit is washed and sparkling.

And Gina, in remarkably similar words: "The energy in my body seemed so powerful . . . My body felt like a powerful machine, that was sparkling with a love vibration."

Mothers may find that they move differently, during the days and weeks after childbirth: "I felt as light as air and although I moved slowly, it was flowingly." "I seemed to be moving as though I was in slow motion."

Along with this slowing come sensations of being soft, small and warm: "During the weeks after his birth I felt a `softness' in myself—my voice and demeanor were even softer." When my own baby was six days old, I wrote about the "hallucination" I kept having, of seeing my hands as his hands, tiny and soft. The parts of my body felt dainty and small as I touched them, as though my hands were sensitized to a baby's miniature dimensions. Aura Joy perceived her body as "small and soft, as if I was a baby too, teaching it how to move." Perhaps these feelings are a kind of physical communion with the baby.

Relaxation may come more easily than usual. "During breastfeeding," a mother recalls, "I relaxed to the point of falling asleep and felt a deep warm feeling." I remember the delicious comfort of leaning back in my armchair and relaxing everywhere, even at the back of my neck where relaxation was so unfamiliar that it felt like a presence.

This enhanced capacity to relax, and the sudden change of body shape and weight and center of gravity, and the light-headedness of fatigue and blood loss, combined with endorphins that help tune out discomfort—perhaps these are enough to explain why some women experience a sensation they describe as being "out of body."

Elizabeth Green recalls "feeling as if I were outside of my body. Like my spirit was watching the physical being—letting it heal, helping it heal." Her labor had been long and recovery was slow: "I think the anemia made me more dizzy, adding to my head seeming different."

Some people actually experience themselves as being "somewhere else" (their stories will be found in Chapter 15). Others use the words "out of body" to express a sense of expansion beyond their physical boundaries, or the feeling of release that comes when one is almost unaware of the body. Jean writes:

> I don't remember how long it lasted but for the first several days I was definitely out of my body. I knew I was exterior to my body—I recognized the feeling. I've been outside of my body before—when I've been extremely happy and during Scientology auditing.
>
> It's hard for me to describe since it's such a subjective experience. An analogy would be the difference between experiencing life by looking down through a tube (being in the body) as opposed to not using the tube.
>
> Usually when I'm not exterior to the body I feel fine and am aware of my self with boundaries that fluctuate—usually right around the outside of my skin, my head. When I'm outside the body I just expand and feel no boundaries. Nothing is surrounding me and I feel pervasive. I don't have perceptions that allow me to see, feel, hear through walls and such, and I can't do it at will. I do have the experience of limitless expansion.

Sensations like these can make us wonder whether there are other dimensions to the body. Do we have an "energy body" that also takes part in childbirth? Claudia Panuthos makes a brief mention of this in her book *Transformation Through Birth: A Woman's Guide* (Bergin & Garvey,1984), when she recommends massage as a healing aid after delivery:

> Surgically delivered and medically interrupted women are even more desperate for touch because of the unavoidable violations to the physical body and the accompanying breakdown of the etheric field, the invisible outer protective energy surrounding the body.

Karen Hand endured severe disturbances, both physical and mental, after her first child's birth. She says:

> Three weeks before my due date my gallbladder went very bad so

emergency surgery was done, first a c-section and appendectomy, then the removal of the gall bladder.

The experience began one day after my son was born. I felt something around my wrist. Thinking it was my hospital bracelets I was frantic about wanting them off. I'd see things moving in my peripheral vision, but when I turned to see what it was, there was nothing there.

I couldn't relax. I would sleep but I'd wake up feeling as though I'd never gone to sleep. I had horrible dreams, after pain medications. It was so bad I forced myself to stay awake.

I had the feeling I was in the wrong body, like I was sitting in the room but it wasn't me. My hands would shake uncontrollably; I'd cry. I would get terrible uncomfortable feelings over the rest of my body and I would keep moving around sometimes quite violently to try and get comfortable. I thought if the feeling didn't stop they'd "put me away."

Karen noticed that the discomfort lessened when her chiropractor was in contact with her. Her husband, attributing the problems to a spirit entity, performed a ritual exorcism after which the distressing symptoms "just gradually stopped," says Karen.

But there are other possible explanations for her experience. She had undergone major surgery under general anesthesia, which perhaps disturbed her metabolism enough to cause these bizarre sensations. The pain medications that brought on nightmares may have been producing other side effects. Could it also be that her etheric field was injured—her energy body out of alignment?

The concept of an energy body became much more real to me after my own daughter's birth. In the last minutes of labor, when I was beginning to feel the exhilaration of pushing, the doctor applied vacuum forceps to the baby's head and pulled her out. Before I could see or touch her, she was hoisted through the air to a table out of sight, where a pediatrician checked her lungs before returning her to us.

In those few moments when the power to give birth was taken from me and my baby was whisked away, some rhythm or connection was lost. It would take time and conscious effort to find it again. In the following weeks, I found myself oddly uncomfortable and thinking obsessively about the delivery. It felt as though there was a gap in my aura—as though the abrupt end of labor and the sudden separation had damaged the field we'd shared so long. I craved my baby right next to me, her feet pressing my abdomen. Her presence eased my tension and loneliness, but it was six months before my womb relaxed and I felt "intact" again.

Is it possible that severing the physical closeness of mother and baby is more traumatic than we realize? We need to learn more about these effects. Breaking the water, speeding birth with vacuum forceps and other ways of altering the pace of labor may disrupt an energy pattern that has its own trajectory, much like a sexual rhythm. Sometimes interference cannot be avoided, but we must reckon with the recoil of such a powerful force.

~ ~ ~

Sensory changes come at various times in the birth cycle. Some begin during pregnancy; some are linked with labor and persist for a while afterward; others begin or intensify a few days later.

The first few minutes after birth are often attended by sensory surprises. This is a time of sudden enormous change, as in Robin Kristufek's description, "The whole world (really my whole focus) shifted: from myself to another small one outside." With this shift of focus comes an altered sense of time. Some women recall a feeling of time suspended:

> Immediately after my son was born and I was looking at him lying on the table between my legs, I felt like time had stopped. It seemed like hours passed while I was looking at him there, but it was only seconds. That instant is embedded in my psyche forever. It was like fireworks, and the band striking up when I just fell in love with him in those seconds immediately after birth.

There are mysterious changes in our perception of light. Could they be caused by the pressure of those final pushes—or do our pupils open wide, letting in a flood of extra light when we see the baby? "As she was born into my husband's hands," one woman says, "a bright light was diffused through the entire birthing area surrounding her, as though she were cradled in the manger." Sue Akerman recalls, "Around the time of delivery, there was a peculiar `brightness' in the room, though the lights were turned off and there was only moderate daylight."

Intense focusing on the baby causes other details to fade away. Sue continues:

> Adrian's father said later that I was reaching for Adrian and saying "Give him to me," which I have no recollection of doing. Also during this time certain details were etched on my memory: Adrian's face and head shape, a remark made by his father about his feet. In my recall of the moments just after this, I said to Adrian's father that he had "left the room" for a few minutes. He says no, in fact he was at my side all that time.

"I didn't hear *anything*," Aura Joy recalls, "not the birds chirping, nothing for a few hours after the birth." And Cheryl Lockwood writes of her own state of mind during labor and just afterward:

> What I do remember most is the altered perceptions of my body— of it not even existing—the whole experience was in my mind and it was an explosion of sounds, visions (sensations turning into sounds/visions) and very little actually escaping my lips. If I could have tape recorded my mind's events ... whenever I spoke it was as if the words weren't from 'me'—I was this incredible universe of sensations and sounds and noises—the voice was from some other level.
>
> When Meghan was born, Robin laid her immediately on my tummy. She was still connected to me through her umbilical cord. I looked at Meghan lying next to my breast and it seemed that the background noises and people's presences became a blur. I can't remember what anyone else was doing or saying except when a statement was directed specifically to me.

Lynne Shank is a mother of four. She too has noticed a change in her awareness at each birth, and finds that "the more quiet and natural the setting, the stronger the altered states." She says:

> When my fourth child was born I was really not able to focus in on anyone or anything except Elizabeth. I was enraptured with her— her smell—her looks—her noises—breathing—body movements. My husband had placed a large metal bowl between my feet and I had had it there for half an hour without even knowing it. He also had done a lot of clean-up and cord clamping and cutting etc. and I was totally unaware of anything or anyone outside an area of about one foot outside myself and Elizabeth who was in my arms. It was as though her vibrations and mine were one. I was so deeply enmeshed into her being that I couldn't look away or think about anything else. She was like a dance we did together.
>
> I could see Elizabeth glowing and growing; I only heard her breathing and growing ... Everything else seemed far away and smooth; everything was pastel colors, not the usual ones.
>
> Just smelling and looking at and holding Elizabeth can still intensify my feelings of altered awareness. The whole world can "go away."

In contrast to the intense and narrowed focus some women experience right after delivery, others describe a sensory expansion that might be called psychedelic.

"Psychedelic" is a word that needs defining. Literally "mind manifesting," it suggests a two-way flow between mind and matter. Everything we perceive seems to be mirroring our inner state, and we feel open to every-thing: the blue of a vase, the sound of music. Psychedelic substances such as LSD have allowed us to explore the fluid, mysterious border between the self and the sensory world. Childbirth and newborn time often give access to a similar state, where our customary isolation may yield to openness and flow.

Many people first notice this change through altered senses. Rebekah Bridge tells of heightened sensory awareness lasting several days when her first child was born. "My experience was subtle, yet extraordinary," she says:

> During labor, birthing and immediately postpartum, it was as though all my senses could hear, feel, smell, see everything for miles. I could sense what the vibes were from all of the people on the block. I could feel God's power within us. I could see, hear, feel, smell, taste the atmosphere as though it were magnified to infinity.
>
> I felt as though I was incredibly aware of my mind and all that it contained—past births and deaths. I felt meshed with the uni-verse. I had no sense of myself as being different or other from any other part of the world. I could feel my body intensely-large, small, beating, bloodrushing, open. I could see through skin, through walls, through dirt, as it were, viewing the vibes of our planet and its atmosphere. Everything was clear and my inner self felt soaring with energy.
>
> It faded after a few days like slow waves. It decreased greatly when I went to sleep for the first time with my baby in my arms. But lingering parts of it are with me still.

In the following story, Aura Joy describes a similar expansive quality of sensory change, again beginning in labor and lasting for several days afterward:

> Each tree "speaks" to me. Each flower "sings" to me. But nothing is anything like the state of consciousness after birth. Your body has been many times spent; you felt reduced to ethereal dust itself, one with particulates, and the hormones working on your system make you feel other than you ever in your life would feel.
>
> I find it very hard to relate just what the feelings were because they are so intangible, but so intense and fecund, fertile, like the overpowering purity of the smell of rich humus soil and the feel of growing things. It feels like the highest calm one could possibly experience. The feeling is it all.
>
> After I pushed the baby out, I was incredibly aware, and felt all new as if I had just been born. My skin felt all soft like a baby's, like I just came out and I looked at the world in what I imagine as when birthed. Incredible—I live again and I didn't have to die—or did I?

But I still have all my knowledge of the last twenty-five years with me and reborn!

True peace filled everyone around. Of course, from the onset of labor, it's as if on acid, all now is still glowing and turning colors and almost pulsing, like a strobe. The baby—I watched him come out and put on my abdomen feeling no emotion or reaction as those feelings all refined into a calm, content, warm, delicate, all's-well-with-the-world-in a soft cocoon that would always surround me, trance-like state.

My midwives suctioned him out and I watched him come alive and respond and I felt like I could feel the world as if I was inside of him, feeling every flicker of his movements. I really felt like I was a baby, too. We said hello and welcomed him. And I remember the feeling of my pure smile.

Nothing like any of this any other time in anyone's life! This is it. I started to shake and my body didn't stop strong shaking and contractions for hours. My muscles had a hard time relaxing. I saw my placenta and ate and drank, I could say it was like in a dream, but it was like in reality. I was extremely aware, acutely with what was happening and as if on acid, mute, smiling, feeling like I was made of silk and on a waterbed world (I was on a hard bed) and transfixed; seeing colors, glows and strobing. They had to sew me up and I would see all kinds of patterns in the air, lines squiggly.

Sean T Ra (the baby) lay on me—eyes closed, facing me. I said, "Ra?!" He opened his eyes and said something and just about smiled, then nuzzled me. I put him on my breast and nearly popped through the roof. He sucked real heavy. I felt joyous tears.

I had lots of visions. Colors flowing, glowing and flashing before me, bathing me and everyone . . . Big popcorn flowers blew up before my eyes. I didn't sleep, just lay or sat stoned for hours.

A person who ran a marathon non-stop for twenty-seven hours (my labor time) would be exhausted. I felt exuberant, unstoppable and in a cocoon, a soft world of light and baby magic. I felt I was magic and everything I was in contact with was magic and special—even the air!

This is how your physical body keeps you from feeling negativity and pain—how wonderful—and leaves you very particularly receptive to your family, your baby and those helping you, keeping your world perspective in shape. I thanked nature, myself, my baby, my man, the midwives, my schoolbus home . . .

"I felt I was magic," says Aura Joy. Such a feeling comes easily in the newborn year: the sense of being in a creative current, or even of being its source.

~   ~   ~

Forty years ago, my mother's hospital stay was the traditional ten days following my birth in Rome. She writes:

> How I loved the villa on that day of homecoming! As an old hand at hospitals, I have always found that home, after a session in those aseptic precincts, takes on a radiance that more than compensates for all clinical adversities. Beauty and warmth and coziness are multiplied in proportion to the severity of the recent ordeal. Old paint looks new. Faded colors glow as if retouched for the occasion. The common smells of herbs and cooking food, of ironings, of garden flowers and furniture polish and wood smoke are incense on the air.

Heightened sensory awareness may come also to mothers who deliver at home, so it can't be attributed only to the hospital stay. "Colors looked vibrant," says Linda; "everything looked alive." And Carla Sunderland says, "Colors were so intense at times I imagined I could even taste them! I had a perception of seeing things living, like walls seeming to breathe." Both of these women remained at home.

Devin and I stayed at the hospital only one day, but when we returned home that night to the house with its lights shining out on the deep snow, I thought our home had never looked so beautiful.

Sensory changes following my son's birth were the most vivid part of my experience. They let me know I was not in just an unusual mood but an altered state of awareness. My response to colors in newborn time was one of the most enjoyable experiences of my life. I am a frustrated artist, never quite sure what I like—a person who will walk into an art gallery and be drawn first to read the small signs hanging near the paintings. My overly verbal mind seems to get in the way of seeing.

During newborn time this was reversed, and I found myself "caught" by colors. I was able to see them in a new way, as if nothing pulled me away from enjoying them. As if I had all the time in the world, just to look.

It was color photographs, with their glossy, light-reflecting surfaces, that first alerted me to the change. I remember a radiant white flower on the cover of a magazine; it seemed to light up the space it occupied in our house. Leafing through magazines to look at photographs became my favorite relaxation. I often held them upside down, to enjoy the colors without the distraction of meaning. I cut out pictures and kept them in a folder near my rocking chair. Certain colors made me relax and breathe deeply, just by gazing into them.

And I knew what I liked. Some pictures had a magnetic energy; sometimes it was concentrated in one small detail—a round cake of soft-looking red soap, the glistening black eyes of a child. Photographs of sunset clouds or silvery rippled reflections in water were irresistible. I discovered that the people who made car advertisements knew all about this: car ads, that year, abounded in gleaming reflecting surfaces, pink and gold clouds and rain-washed roads.

There was a definite progression in the way colors attracted me. Day by day I would "tune in" different ones—first the peachy pinks and aqua, then dark blue-black and red-violet. At first I felt a strong aversion to bright yellow and kelly green, but as the process went on, almost every color became beautiful.

It seemed that the most appealing colors were those of the baby, from peachy skin and blue veins to the smoky blue of his eyes. But I still can't explain why I saw pink overtones on other colors, rosy reflections in silver spoons, and lavender, pink and light blue washing over the white walls of our room, or why silvery surfaces looked soft and liquid.

I noticed that each eye's vision was different. My left eye saw warm, rosy tones where the right eye saw colder ones. Sometimes, oddly enough, this was reversed, and rarely they were balanced. I practiced looking with my left eye alone until the warm rosiness became my usual perception.

It still puzzles me that the changes in color vision seem to be rather uncommon, or at least seldom talked about. It puzzles me all the more because evidently they are part of our common knowledge, even though unspoken.

I had grown up thinking that pink and blue for babies was sentimental nonsense, and planned to surround mine with yellow and green! But when I held my baby and looked at the world with new eyes, to my surprise it was the traditional baby colors that were the most delightful and perhaps most healing. (In fact, it has been found that certain shades of pink and blue induce relaxation.) The softly colored cards and gift-wraps arriving in each day's mail were confirmation that, even though no one seemed to be aware of it, I was sharing in a state well known to humankind and well worth supporting with a little pastel tenderness.

Other visual changes after my son's birth were even more mysterious. Drops of silver appeared to fall from the ceiling of our living room, looking like streaks of heavy light. Similar experiences are reported by other people. "Slight hallucinations," one mother called them: "seeing a flash of something out of the corner of my eye and knowing it wasn't really there—flashes of light, images, colors."

But when I looked at the particle board of my bedside stand and saw hundreds of baby faces in its random splotches, it was easy to realize that I was seeing images of my own preoccupation. The process of "projection" had never been so obvious.

Lisa Torchio Oviatt recalls a moment in the first week after her son's birth:

> Our bed at the time was on a raised platform even with a small window. I can remember lying there in the heat looking out the

window, and through that shimmering, sultry heat, among the leaves of the trees were hundreds of baby faces. I actually found it a bit disturbing . . .

Lisa found her visual perception changed in another way as well, during that first week:

> Eric's birth was a long twenty-five hours of real labor with three previous days of warm-up. The culmination was sheer exhaustion and elation upon his birth. The excitement and family circumstances led to a week after with little to no sleep. I feel the nervous excitement and true sleep deprivation led to the altered state.
>
> The "other awareness" began after returning home, twelve hours after Eric was born. For the first week I became aware of the infant in us all. This manifested itself in people's faces, hands and mannerisms. This is difficult to articulate, but I'll try to explain further.
>
> What seemed to be happening was that I was looking through other eyes with a whole new perspective. That perspective was filled with the infant world. I could see individuals as they were as infants. This included my mother, father, husband, brother and several friends. My father in particular stood out among the rest. (After trying to explain it to my father, who didn't appear to really grasp what I was experiencing, I felt a strong connection to my grandmother, his mother, who was about three hundred miles away.)
>
> I should state that I had almost no previous experience with infants before my son. I had never changed a diaper before Eric's. The intense observation of a newborn's every action may have led to this increased, heightened awareness of the infant in us all.

Like Lisa, I was a novice at newborns, and I too saw people as sweet and babylike, their arms looking tiny and making those endearing, ineffectual movements that babies make. Even forks and spoons and cups would suddenly look small and cute, so that I felt motherly toward everything around me.

My vision was so changed, in fact, that it was sometimes hard to recognize people; I saw them as if for the first time. I remember waiting for the doctor to come into the room at my two-week check-up and feeling very curious, for I realized I had no idea what he was going to look like.

I seemed to be able to read people's state of mind in their faces, and noticed especially whether they were seeing with both eyes. People who were distracted looked grey, with eyes that seemed to look in two different directions.

With my second child's birth, I was determined to pay attention to sensory changes and try to understand them better. My vision changed in some of the same ways, but the effects lasted only three days instead of three weeks. Leafing through a magazine one day, I saw each page flash pink, then turn white again. I wrote:

> It is as if my eyes were adding light to everything they see. I looked at a photograph I first saw several days ago, and the parts that I saw then as very dark brown now look much lighter!
>
> The vision of baby faces everywhere is coming today, and when I had Devin it came with the same timing—three days after the beginning of milk. The color and shininess effects too are the same; the colors that appealed to me then are the same now. Pink, blue-green, ivory white, peach and a soft faded red.
>
> And in the same way, I like cleaning up little patches where I see beauty (that's been staring me in the face all this time) obscured by a little dust and grime: things I have seen every day for years and not appreciated. In this state, I don't do "housework" because everything is so ugly, dirty and demanding—I enjoy doing it because everything is so beautiful it is a pleasure to touch and take care of it.

~   ~   ~

People mention visual changes most often, but they speak of altered perceptions through other senses as well. Some women experience a general heightening: "All senses were heightened; it was a definite `natural high.'" Patricia, an adoptive mother, noticed "more visual awareness, awareness of environmental sounds, changes in texture—touch." Trina Simon didn't realize she was still in an altered state a few days after the birth:

> . . . until I stepped out of my home--my own little world. I sat on the balcony with a friend one day, and immediately became very aware of all the sounds of nature (trees, birds, ocean) that were quite a ways away from my apartment complex; and I said, "I'm still really high."

The sense of hearing seems to change with our changing focus of attention. Home from the hospital with my baby daughter, I lay down to rest while she slept. Knowing that Nick would take care of everything, I slipped out of the mother's habit of identifying and responding to all the ambient sounds. Drowsily relaxed, I heard sounds in a different way than ordinarily. It was almost like hearing through water, or a thicker atmosphere than usual.

Laurie Russell noticed parallel effects in seeing and hearing: "I had visual changes—sometimes the baby and I would be very clear and sharp but everything around was fuzzy. The same with sound. In fact sometimes people in the same room with me sounded like they were far away."

With ears sensitized to the small noises of a newborn, we experience new pleasures and discomforts. "The TV was bothering me a lot more than usual," says Linda. "I wanted it to be really quiet." In newborn time we may respond differently to music. The sliding, caressing sounds of a George Harrison song seemed to melt my heart and move me deeper into a warm and blissful state. Martha Isaacson says, "My shift in awareness was intensified as I nursed the baby and as I listened to classical music—especially when I did both together. Music spoke to me in a special, moving way."

Newborns are able to recognize the smell of their own mother's breast within a few days after birth; not surprisingly, mothers speak of the attraction of their own baby's smell. Laurie Russell says:

> My sense of smell was very acute following my last baby. I decided to let myself feel whatever felt right during birth and after, and found myself wanting to smell the baby a lot. It sounds kind of funny now but I enjoyed smelling her for months. (In fact I still do!)

Holly Piper noted a similar heightening: "I would smell flowers that no one else noticed—from a distance or passing a certain area in a car."

No doubt many women cherish memories of a special meal during that first week after childbirth. "My sense of taste must have been heightened," recalls one mother, "for nothing has ever tasted better than the breakfast-in-bed I enjoyed each morning. In my last weeks of pregnancy, I had cooked and frozen dozens of cheese blintzes. My husband would saute them in butter and serve them with dark sweet cherries and sour cream and a cup of milky tea, and it was ambrosia!"

As with taste, so with the sense of touch. People often mention its increased sensitivity. But its most mysterious change has to do with perceiving a special texture in the atmosphere: "The air had a texture I could feel." This merges into an experience that seems to go beyond the separate senses, involving all of them in a new way, as we shall see.

~ ~ ~

There is a special sensory shift that sometimes happens in the first few days after childbirth which might be called "perceiving a presence." I was writing in the early morning quiet, when my baby Roselyn was not yet two days old:

> There's an atmosphere I become aware of, that I have felt before, that feels like "angels' wings": soft, warm and in motion. It seemed

to begin with my first drowsy naps in the hospital. My body was full of left-over tension and muscle jerks from labor, as if labor connected me to an energy bigger than my own. Then, coming back home, there's that tendency I always notice after being in an unusual environment, to misinterpret sounds, a bit of sensory disorientation. Drowsily resting on the couch with my family stirring around in the house, I hear a lot of sounds in a different way than ordinarily. And when else do I ever stay resting still and soft for long enough to notice the density, the thickness and richness of the moment . . . almost oiliness . . . angelic presence.

Where had I felt that atmosphere before? A few times in the ambience of extraordinary people—but mostly in the weeks after Devin's birth.

First I noticed a pervading warmth throughout my body; then it seemed to extend beyond me and to fill the entire house with a soft, warm presence. I remember lying on the couch for long periods of time basking in it. "It is sometimes like swimming or floating in a sea of bliss—like feeling the presence of God in the house as a rosy aura of love and a deep soft breathing."

Other people too have perceived a mysterious presence during new-born time:

> I have often said in reference to the first three days together as a family that there was a presence, "something in the air," quite unexplainable, that was so thick "it could be cut with a knife."
> - Pam Myers

> I remember the few days following Casey's birth, that there was a kind of electricity in the air in my home. It is hard finding the right words to describe it. I'm not sure if everyone felt it or if it was only me. I felt as though there was a "glow" in the air, almost a buzzing sound, that I felt rather than heard. It was like being in a nice, pleasant, secure fog. Time stood still. A very peaceful feeling . . .
> - Diane Dougherty-Keller

Sometimes a mother feels a presence or an energy emanating from herself and the baby, or enfolding them: "It was like a magnetic force surrounding us . . ." "Incredible love pulsated around us."

Kathi prefaces her story by noting that her two deliveries were very different in terms of attendants and setting. Her first child was born by caesarean, attended by two obstetricians, a pediatrician, an anaesthesiologist, two nurses and one husband. The second baby she delivered in a birthing room, assisted by four women: a midwife, a nurse, a sister and a friend. Nevertheless, she says "the postpartum altered state was very similar under both sets of circumstances":

There was a very strong sense of euphoria and heightened sensory awareness. A feeling like energy was emanating from mother and child and affecting everyone in proximity (females much more willing to verbalize/share in state than males). Much of it seemed to be a direct result of states during labor and delivery, but there was a very strong healing quality which was new after delivery.

In the first birth, I felt a disruption in the state when separated from the newborn due to hospital protocols. If you could "see" energy, it would not be unlike some of the effects of Kirlian photography when a leaf part is removed.

The presence may seem to have a protecting quality. Erika felt a protecting presence right after the birth of her son, who arrived before the midwife:

My son Sage was born quite quickly with virtually no strong contractions. I just got off the phone with the midwife and waters broke, the head began crowning and at that point it became obvious we'd be delivering the baby ourselves. An incredible rush of strength and confidence came over me; we went upstairs to crouch to deliver his head and sit back on pillows to deliver his body.

I felt totally protected, timeless, blessed, and also noticed the light changed and everything looked softer and golden. As Sage nursed and checked out his new world I felt a cone of protection over our room.

Jann Light describes a presence she perceived during the ritual circumcision ceremony for her son:

In spite of the discomfort I felt at the operation itself, following it, during all the ceremony and prayers and blessings, I was aware that what is referred to as the Shechina, a name for God's protecting presence, came into the house. It settled down into our living room through the ceiling and wrapped each person in the room like a loving blanket. It was a very special heartening experience for me, especially since I had a few doubts about the circumcision. This seemed to confirm we had made the right decision.

One mother wondered whether anyone else noticed the "glow" in her home. Here is a story that suggests other people may indeed feel something unusual in the presence of a newborn:

I wanted to tell you about an experience I had in St. Paul at Eastertime. While visiting relatives there, I called a friend who I knew was expecting her third child at any time. It turned out she had just had her new baby girl at home three hours before I called.

I visited her and her husband and their hours-old child. It was a magical experience. They were gathered in an upstairs bedroom, the room where the child had been born, and as I climbed the stairs I could almost feel an ineffable glowing presence increase with each step. I can't explain the wondrous feeling within the room, the glow from the mother and child, the sparkle in the father's eyes, like they all had haloes that lit up the room.

I had never visited a baby so young before (except my own) so I don't know whether these feelings of love and luminescence can be sensed around every newborn, or only home-birthed newborns, or only the home-birthed newborns of former acidheads. (Maybe all that LSD really did cause some subtle chromosome changes!) Or maybe seeing them just awakened my own memories of birth magic, as a kind of flashback.

5

Changing Awareness: The Central Shift

*I*s there a typical change of awareness during the newborn year? The answer seems to be yes. Although we will see some extreme alterations of mind and mood, there is a subtler and quieter change that is much more common.

What many parents experience is a shift away from intellectual, logical thinking and toward a more sensuous, intuitive mode. This new state of mind may persist for several weeks or even months, seldom longer than a year, although it can open doors to more lasting changes.

Looking back, I realize this shift of awareness began for me in late pregnancy. "I suppose the two sides of my brain are competing," I remarked a few days before the birth, as I found myself beginning to stutter, and not wanting to read as much as usual. Instead, I spent hours winding my yarn collection into balls and hanging them on the wall for the pleasure of seeing their colors and combinations.

For weeks after Devin's birth, I was in a condition I described to myself as "my natural state of consciousness." It felt as though a new area of my brain was awake. I had an almost physical sense of functioning from a whole and balanced awareness. On the other hand, I could never remember to put away the leftovers, and had to post reminders on the bathroom mirror: "Stove turned off? Thermostat turned down?"

The following stories illustrate this shift of mental mode. Lorna Rutherford experienced many of its effects both positive and problematic. Her background is important, for difficulties tend to arise where altered awareness meets the agenda of pre-baby life:

> I'm thirty-four, married with two sons, four years old and two months old. I've worked with deaf children for many years and am currently working at a mental health clinic part time. I'm at a crossroads in my career. To complete work on my Marriage and Family and Child Counseling licence I'll need to complete a second Master's and I'm not sure I want to do that. So right now I'm putting that on hold while I'm enjoying my family.
>
> I haven't had many unusual experiences after childbirth as much as I've had an altered state of awareness, of sorts. It's a little difficult to describe.

Some studies in psychology have said we can hold seven units of information in our minds at one time—an eighth unit comes and one unit will "drop out" (or go into storage), leaving seven again.

During pregnancy and after childbirth I feel as if I can only hold two to four units of information at one time. I become much more focused on my priorities of the moment and less important details are forgotten. Occasionally, especially immediately after the birth of my first child, I would say things and wonder if they made sense.

I also respond more to my intuitive experiencing of events after childbirth than I normally do. And again, with not always holding on to all the "units" of information. One of the most obvious experiences with this was shortly after the birth of my first son. A coworker with the last name of Chris came to visit. She has always reminded me of another friend whose first name is Chris. I spent the whole visit calling her Chris and it wasn't until I was walking her to her car that I realized I had been doing that.

Another aspect of this focusing of mine is that I have difficulty seeing the different facets of my life as a connected whole. It's as if I have different realities going on at the same time and I have a difficult time switching from one to another. I don't feel "split," I just have a hard time changing gears. I'm almost six weeks postpartum at the moment and I resumed seeing a client a few nights ago. It took me a few hours to mentally prepare for it and I found it difficult to be fully present during the session. I'm finding that I'm forgetting to complete details that need to be done.

After the birth of our first son I had to take some classes during my year's maternity leave. I had the same experience then, and it was more intense. I disliked having to "switch gears" or "change realities." I wanted to stay home, even though I had chosen to go to the classes and wanted to complete them.

I also feel a definite introspection and drawing into my family occurring. It began in both pregnancies near the end of the third trimester and continued on after the birth.

Growing up, we had numerous cats. When one or another was pregnant, it was not uncommon to find her in the back of the closet in the rag box or in a dresser drawer quietly waiting to give birth. I feel like one of those cats, needing a familiar place with familiar people, and more quietness and calm.

The principal change for Lorna was "being more responsive and aware of my intuitive self—and trusting that part of me." And the cause of her experience?

I'm not sure. It may be an inner protection or wisdom that has helped me focus on nurturing this new little life, along with myself and my family. I think it had a positive effect on my relationship with my children. It has helped me slow down and enjoy my mothering. I was slightly embarrassed at times when I seemed a bit out of touch with what was going on, but I basically accepted what was happening to me. I wondered about it but it felt okay. But I haven't talked to many people about this experience; I didn't want to risk their misunderstanding or judging me.

Another woman gives a revealing answer to the question, "At the time it was happening, how did you interpret your experience?"

"In general," Robin Kristufek replies, "I didn't interpret it much at all. I was just in it, feeling it. That was part of it, that I felt so right-brained (non-intellectual)."

This state of mind probably has the greatest impact on a person who has favored a rational, analytic style. Joan Pasch found the adjustment stressful and yet ultimately beneficial:

I grew up on a farm and was the oldest of three daughters. I have two Master's degrees, one in German and one in Linguistics. When I was in my twenties I liked children but felt impatient with them. When my only daughter was born I found I had more patience than before, because she seemed so wonderful.

After Lauren was born I was so exhausted that I could not care for her (my husband stayed at the hospital and did everything), but I found I could not sleep. Labor began around ten on a Friday morning, she was born the next morning at four A.M., yet I could not sleep Saturday night and only a few hours Sunday night. I felt very tired but not sleepy. I wasn't really preoccupied but calm, and would listen to see if she was awake or what. Then for the next two years I would waken at the slightest noise—she didn't sleep through the night for a long time.

I didn't have the Baby Blues as far as resenting my baby, but I found that never getting enough sleep and having sleep interrupted all the time caused some mental changes. I became more self-sacrificing and was unable to be very intellectual in conversations. I still read but my circumstances were training me never to follow a thought to a logical conclusion.

It seemed very right and instinctual and like I had no choice but to submit to this different emotional and mental state, or to reject my baby and what my body was telling me. I think it made me a better mother—it was my "baby time" and to do it right that's all I could handle. But I had some doubts sometimes, it seemed like I was losing my intelligence. The negative part is that it caused my husband to have less respect for me for several years. Now everything is okay but he is opposed to having a second child because of it.

Lauren and I have always been close. And I am still "steady" in a way I wasn't before. Having a child really did change my life, and for the better. I am more mature, and I know better how to be patient with myself. I like kids, but having my own helped me emotionally—as I mothered her I was also mothering myself, simultaneously.

Anara's experience was similar to Joan's, and she advises, "Don't be surprised if your intellect goes on vacation. This is no time for rationality but rather for intuition and practicing patience (which you'll need more as they grow into toddlers)." She adds:

I hope that your project can encourage acceptance of other states of being without closing doors to women again. I felt like my husband was startled—and disappointed—to find me so non-intellectual in the months following each birth. Sleep deprivation certainly is part of the brew. And those omnipresent, anonymous Hormones.

There are other ways to look at this phenomenon of finding ourselves suddenly "non-intellectual." When we operate in an intellectual mode, we deal easily with abstract ideas and intangibles. During the newborn year we may be biologically influenced to give less attention to anything not of immediate concern. We conserve our attention and energy for the needs of the moment.

Many women feel that sleep deprivation plays a major role in causing these changes. Rita is one:

I found the period after my first child, my daughter Suzanne, a time of great adjustment. I had just graduated from college and had to shift from the productive, disciplined days of school to the slow, unstructured days of baby care. I remember being of a totally different frame of mind and I found it a little frightening.

Suzanne woke up to nurse every one and a half hours for the first three months of her life. I felt like a zombie much of the time. Friends commented that I talked much less than before. I know that I did not think in the same clear, linear manner that I had before. I was no longer able to reflect on myself for a long period of time. I temporarily lost my ability to analyze—politically or socially. I felt the nurturer and was encompassed by my daughter's need for me.

In the long run, I think this was a helpful change for me. I have become much more flexible as a person. I can adjust to different situations more easily now, and I am more able to accept my emotional state for what it is rather than fighting it or intellectualizing it. But the first months of these new demands on me I remember as mixed.

These changes to our state of mind can cause some surprising difficulties. Kelly recalls:

Having been a fairly aggressive woman, able to speak my mind, good at problem solving and mathematics, I was very surprised to find that I was unable to visually count up more than ten objects without losing track and that even simple mathematics was impossible for almost a year. Since I was in the middle of building a house and attempting to be the contractor coordinating all the ordering of materials, subcontractors and so forth, the loss of my mathematical and planning abilities was difficult.

There may be communication problems and friction with others, even those closest to us. Robin Kristufek, after describing how perfect and wise her newborn son appeared, goes on to say:

Another matter was how I viewed the rest of the normal world for a while. Other people mostly seemed so clumsy, cloddy, slow, mundane, almost stupid. I felt impatient with them. Usually I like other people a lot, so this made relationships a little strained and weird for a while.

Dealing with people who have no connection with the baby can be hardest of all. As Richard Myers put it, "The people we had to deal with were not a part of the event, and therefore communication was difficult. Also, returning to the `normal' world was difficult."

Even the mechanics of communication may become elusive, as Mary Kohl describes:

From what I can remember, I was fairly normal after the birth of my first child; it was after my second child was born that I had the unusual experiences.

I had the darndest time talking, believe it or not—probably because half of my consciousness was someplace else. My sentence structure was terrible, I used the wrong words; I thought I must have sounded so mixed up that I just kept my mouth shut. My handwriting became illegible. I even made a simple math error on our checking account which escaped detection during this period.

Tasks that once were automatic may now seem difficult to accomplish. Mary goes on to say:

> Some days I sure wandered around the house like a zombie. My husband said he should have made a film of me just getting a meal ready. I'd head in one direction for something, then in midstream totally forget what it was, start babbling about something, and end up doing something other than what I started out to do. It probably took me half an hour just to set the table.
>
> Driving the car was done sort of "robotically" during the four or five weeks after the birth. I always felt so paranoid; I sometimes would panic and get the brake and the clutch mixed up. The part that had me the most worried was the "talking" part. I was always a bit worried that I'd never sound like an educated person again.

Laurie Russell recalls the weeks following childbirth:

> I felt different than the other people out in the hustle bustle world. I felt very safe and secure at home but like I almost couldn't handle things like driving in traffic. I had to force myself to concentrate on the traffic while driving—like I was operating on some other plane. My only accident ever and my only ticket ever both happened a few weeks after I gave birth—different babies. I could anticipate my babies' every need but the outside world seemed so nuts.

Only three days after the birth of her first child, Gail attempted to drive and shop alone at a large department store. A feeling of "loss of reality" overcame her:

> I became anxious that I would faint or get sick. As I was driving I feared losing control of the car. I felt desperately alone, became frantic and had to hurry home to my husband and baby. I came home and lost emotional control—tears and so on.

We've seen some of the disadvantages of this mind-state; nevertheless, it seems to ease the transition into parenthood. Sue Akerman recalls the week after her baby's birth: "I had lost a lot of blood and was on strong pain medication. I wore a catheter tube and an IV tube. Yet I recall feeling that I was on 'automatic'; attending to Adrian's needs seemed effortless for me."

The altered state may be so unobtrusive that it is noticed only when it begins to fade away, or when one tackles the activities (such as math or driving) that it seems to hamper. A mother writes:

> My experience was so subtle that I wasn't aware of it until I read about your questionnaire and started thinking back. I'm

aware now that for about two weeks I was in a very peaceful, blissful, relaxed state. Time seemed suspended. It was as if there was no "right" or "wrong" thing to do, but rather I was in touch with what I wanted or needed to do and did it.

A newborn's wants and needs are the same—maybe I was picking that up from Christina and using that energy for me, too. I suppose the suspension of time and feeling of other worldliness can be explained by the fact that I did not leave the house for a week and was up nursing a baby every two hours around the clock, but I doubt that's all of it.

It was a spiritual/religious sort of thing; a little glimpse of heaven maybe, that Christina brought along. My life was so full of peace and love that day to day hassles just vanished—not that they didn't exist, but rather my perspective was changed.

Holly Piper enjoyed a similar mood: "I just watched what happened and if I felt a need to act or react I would, if not I just let it go. I felt I was becoming more in touch with myself and the ancient rhythms of the earth."

Often there is a sense that time is altered or suspended. "In reading back over my journal," says Anne Calajoe, "I find statements that the first month was like a time warp—`October totally vanished.' I was completely unhinged from time; there was no framework from which to remember—everything was continuous and blended together."

"Those first few days with my newborn," another woman recalls, "time seemed to stand absolutely still. It was just the two of us in rapture. My husband had been moved and awed by the birth and was feeling buoyant, my house was quiet with few demands. My child and I were given the time and space to create our own universe."

One may feel set apart, in a special time and place, and yet more than ever in touch with reality, as Elizabeth Green writes:

> I am thirty years old, living with my mate. First child, Abraham, born November 1986. I lead a spiritual inner life of prayer and meditation. Do a lot of walking, swimming, canoeing, cross-country skiiing. I have a BS in Business and run an office for a development corporation—accounting, marketing. (I quit Monday. My five-month-old has been with me at the office until last month. Now I can't stand it. I love my job and the stimulus but don't want to miss this time in his life.)
>
> During my pregnancy I was doing a lot of meditation and practicing to stay in the moment. As time went on that got easier because of the physical aspect of pregnancy—like getting up four times in the night to pee.
>
> I would pray to God each day (I will use the term "God" for my spiritual beliefs for simplicity), meditating on a white protective

light to surround my belly and to help me to be an open vessel to receive love and guidance and to give it as well from Him—not me. (It's great to write about this. I've been wearing makeup and nylons, and working at the computer and calculator for too many months. You'd think I wore Indian print dresses and braids.)

Anyway—during my pregnancy I had very primal feelings. Shelter, good food, warmth, exercise . . . but also at times a sensation of floating. Being a part of the atmosphere—like a tree, rather than a thinking human being. I needed to be outside a lot.

One Sunday, I knew I was going to go into labor that day. I just felt it, and went to a friend's who lived by a lake. I was so aware of everything—but not trying to be, just being a part of it all. My labor was twenty-eight hours long, with twelve hours of one and a half minute contractions every three minutes after my water had broken. Then it stopped. Then I had pitocin . . . tried every position to push him out and he wouldn't come, and he was born by a full episiotomy and forceps four hours later.

All during that time I felt that I was in a trance, yet hearing and knowing what was going on around me. Feeling each person's emotions and judgements. Like I was in their shoes and knew what they thought about the situation, even with my eyes closed. The moment he was born I remembered every conversation I'd had with other mothers.

Once home with Abraham I was out of it physically for a few weeks. Between the labor and being anemic I was in bed a lot.

I became extremely dependent on John, which I had never allowed myself to do in the past. But my actions were unconscious — natural, as were his. My head quit talking to me, "You should do that . . . Don't depend on others . . ." The old voices stopped. There was no future and no past except for the birth.

People would come and go and I would have to try to bring myself back to this plane where they were and where I used to be. Then they'd leave and I could relax and be in reality. That place where even today seems more real than anywhere I've ever been. I could just BE in the shower. Feeling the water, smelling, hearing, tasting the moment. And Abraham was GOD—is GOD—is REALITY. This little human being who knows no future or past, or the difference between a dollar and a napkin.

At three weeks he was operated on for two hernias and pyloric stenosis. I stayed on the floor in the hospital playroom one weekend after watching him vomit for two days straight. He had been to the doctor's after six hours of vomiting, but we had to wait to make sure it wasn't a flu and then wait for the surgeon to see us and wait for the surgery. Yet I was never "waiting." I was just there with him, that moment.

This feeling started to go away, because it was as if I had to make it go away—and it was painful to do that. I was planning for the future: "How will I bottlefeed him if he won't take a bottle." Worrying about babysitters, work . . . I cried a lot because going back to the "other world" wasn't where I was meant to be and yet I felt that that was where I had to go. Eventually this present world I'm in now took over and it doesn't feel as right. Yet I have learned to integrate the post-baby life more. It feels good now to have experienced the other and strive to balance the two, because I wouldn't be able to cope in today's society in the other place. (I find that a little sad.)

Elizabeth's story reveals the strong similarity between altered awareness in newborn time and the mystical experience. Mystical consciousness perceives a unity behind the multiplicity of things—an essence that connects them. We may perceive this unified "field" in many ways, such as a sound encompassing all sounds. The sense of timelessness is a similar effect, where divisions of past and future are absorbed by the vast present.

Martha Isaacson had sought this mystical awareness in many ways, but never expected to find it through childbirth. She writes:

My first child was born eight years ago. He was a posterior baby and it was a long labor. I had Lamaze preparation and Ken was with me. Other than that, it was a pretty conventional hospital birth.

I was thrilled to pieces to have a beautiful boy—and to have the labor over! I was too excited to sleep after the baby went to the nursery and Ken went home.

This was the beginning of the most extraordinary spiritual experience of my life. I experienced the world with an amazing intensity. Everything was alive, glowing in its separateness and uniqueness and yet part of everything else.

Martha's altered state of awareness began within a few hours of the birth and ended "about ten days later, gradually, and after many ups and downs." She says:

I felt other people's emotions as if they were my own. I knew a great closeness and openness with my husband. I felt his grief at the loss of his job as in the saying, "When one cries, the other will taste salt."

I saw the world as being separated into the natural and the supernatural. There were points where the two intersected and these were called birth and death. What a privilege to be able to be at one of those points, to be used as a channel for new life. With a

81

background in literature, I had the greatest respect for creativity in all the arts. But how paltry even the greatest poem seemed, next to the power to bring forth life.

I saw every birth as an Incarnation—God expressing himself (herself/itself) as man. The Incarnation did not seem like a single, historical event, but something which happens at every birth. I sat by the hour nursing my baby, listening to classical music, and swept away by the wonder of it all.

I realized that I was having a mystical experience. At points I found it frightening and thought that it was a state close to being mentally ill. The amazing intensity and duration of the perceptual shift became a concern to me. I understand now the comparisons that have been made between mystical experience and schizophrenia.

Even when my baby slept, I found it hard to sleep. When so many exciting things are happening in your head, it's hard to turn it off. Sleep deprivation gets you high, so I don't know if this was a result or a cause.

On the practical level, perhaps the long labor released chemicals within the body. On the spiritual level, I see this experience as a gift from God, the great Mother, the Cosmos, or my own share in unified consciousness.

I had had hints of this perceptual shift in the past. I had perceived an exciting unifying energy running through all of life. During my post-birth shift in awareness I was in touch with this energy in a deeper and more profound way than ever before.

I would like to say that I became a holy person as a result of this—but I didn't. I have clung to this memory, though, during hard times in my life, especially deaths. I feel more convinced than ever that there is a meaning to life. If we were able to enter the "altered state" at will, we would be more closely in contact with this meaning.

This was the peak experience of my life. I would like to go "there" again, but I somehow doubt that I ever will.

Caring for a baby demands so much, but in return it can give a new ability to live in the moment and savor it. I often think of a letter my friend Laurel wrote when her firstborn Nicholas was small:

It's very late at night and my mind is boggled and half asleep. My life is so full of activity during the day that this is the only time I have for writing. Today I canned two dozen quarts of plum jam. Very little time any more for thinking, contemplating, reflecting. Get all that done before a baby—impossible!

How dear are the minutes in the day when I can let my thoughts, fantasies, dreams float out into the blue and mingle together.

These pleasures of life, which I had always taken for granted, have now become sweeter than ever.

Nicholas has perhaps changed my life more dramatically and totally than anything else. I seem to be conscious of every moment in life, one way or another, pleasant or otherwise, exasperated or delighted.

With all its demands, this time offers a chance to discover our own capacity for peacefulness. Mary recalls:

During Emily's long evening nursings I would practice a yoga concentration technique which is similar to mantra practices. The goal is to still the body and mind, the breath and heartbeat, before meditation. I would become so still during these "nursing meditations" that I couldn't remember when I'd last breathed and my pulse was barely perceptible. It became so much a part of me that any time I concentrated on that technique, even when I wasn't sitting or meditating, I would immediately go into that calm state, after only a breath or two. The instant accessibility of deep peace was new.

It was such a beautiful and inspiring time for me, I felt so close to the Divine, that I sometimes wonder if my desire for another child stems from a yearning to recreate those peaceful times.

I too found peace readily available in the days after my daughter Roselyn's birth. I could lie back in my lounge chair, look up into the leaves beyond the window and instantly enter a peaceful, calm, almost breathless place such as I've touched only rarely in deep meditation. I felt the "inner light" more than I had before, and could feel it pouring out of my eyes.

"The 'psychedelic' component of my altered awareness came and went fairly quickly this time," I wrote. "But I had more of an inner realization—something to keep. I felt the light from my eyes pumping light into the things seen around me. That means to live in the inner light and to be continually creative. It was altogether less of a 'show' but more of an awakening: an awakening to my own responsibility to choose that heavenly life by my own actions."

In this state I felt I could remain forever within my own house and garden and never run out of interesting things to do and beautiful things to enjoy. One reason I value this change of awareness is that it offers part of the solution to our human predicament. It brings out resources that help us to live gracefully with less demand on earth's energies: the ability, for example, to find peace and pleasure in the simplest things.

6

A Sense Of New Connections

With the arrival of a child, both parents may notice a change in their relationship with another, to other people and the world in general. They may discover a new awareness of nature and of their own place in it. It is as though that remarkable feeling of *connectedness* spreads outward in widening circles from their bond with the baby.

When I fell in love with our newborn son, he was like a window opening to the world. As my husband said, "He has brought a feeling of being more connected with the entire community . . . with all life."

One day I received a letter with a stamp commemorating W.C. Fields. Remembering his famous line, I marveled at its unintended wisdom: "When you've seen one baby, you've seen 'em all!" The love we felt for our son seemed to extend outward with no particular boundary. I thought how the energy generated by parents must be nourishing the whole community of creatures on earth. When I began gathering other people's stories, I discovered that my husband and I were not the only ones to feel that bonding to our baby bonded us to the whole world.

Just after giving birth, a tenderness prevails. The same receptivity that attunes us to the newborn makes us more sensitive to other people. As mother and father, we may feel a strengthening of bonds and deeper relationship with one another:

> I felt very in love and tender toward my husband. Also sorry because I was sad he couldn't experience it the wonderful way I could.

> I experienced an incredible connectedness with the baby's father, which he still talks about.

Such feelings of love and kinship may go on expanding to include many others. A mother whose second child was born at home says, "I was filled with a gratefulness to be alive, and a feeling of warmth and love toward all those around me. My friends were helping us out so much . . ."

Ideala Colgate's only child was born nearly fifty years ago, but she has

85

never forgotten the intense love she felt for the baby and everyone else. "People looked beautiful to me," she says. "My sister came to see me and she said she never felt more beautiful in all her life. I felt more alive than ever, and where I had been more self-centered before, I became more outgoing and concerned for others."

More than a year after her first child's birth, Jettie Regnier found her awareness was still dramatically altered since becoming a mother:

> I feel strong family connections. I think of my maternal grand-mother very much (she died when I was twenty years old). I often think I see her in crowds.
>
> When we watch TV and someone is killed (as happens so often on TV) I nearly cry or do cry every time. I never used to do that. Human life seems so valuable to me now. Everything living is so precious.
>
> I find these changes very exciting and mystifying. I wonder—do all mothers (and fathers) feel this way?

In my own pre-baby years, I often thought the attachment of parents to their children was a narrow, limiting thing. I tried to "open my heart" to others by various means, but never felt the reality behind the phrase—until my own child was born. Kate Mareck writes:

> Having a child has helped me spiritually more than any book or technique I've tried. I feel as if every baby were my baby, and I feel most sharply that—what—we're all one? I am you and you are me?
>
> I have a new, deeper love for all people. All baby plants and animals are my baby. I have a stronger sense now, a surety, of a Natural Order, a Universal Love, permeating everything. I have stronger values, I've lost much wishy-washyness. I feel very blessed to have this incredible opportunity to grow more fully—a chance to let go of "me." I am grateful to my daughter and to God for this chance to live, day-by-day, the ideals to which I aspire.

Through our newborn child, we can touch the world. In Ina May Gaskin's book, *Spiritual Midwifery*, a father speaks of feeling connected with others through his newborn, and subsequently with something even more universal. Mark says:

> Holding Louisa for the first time was the most awesome part for me. Her eyes opened right away and it looked like the Universe being unfolded before my eyes. Her face would go through many changes so that she looked like different people that I knew, and I felt telepathic with those folks through her. One time she looked just like my mother, and she felt just like my mother in a peaceful

place, and I saw that place in Louisa that was in all those people and could feel connected and One with the entire Universe through her.

The time of birth, as one mother said, "might just well be the best time to grasp or try to understand our connection to all things in the universe, where and why we fit in, the spiritual specialness of creating a new life, the privilege of being part of the greater whole."

~　　~　　~

Became the tulip; slid down a long
cool petal of apricot.
Anthony and I have been
watching the cartoon movies again.
Silver flashes coming off the tulip.
Bedside daffodils are too beautiful
to be so silent.
We are in awe of your son,
they said.

In the garden, the sage plant
explained itself and I dreamt
a nursing session under its leaves.
Anthony and I are cave bears again.
Our bedroom is a sacred nest;
smell burning leaves and deep rich earth.
Someplace inside of me
this all has a reason for being so beautiful.

Alicia's poem was written one week after her baby Anthony's birth; it reveals her intimate feeling for nature. In pregnancy and newborn time she often felt herself drawn into plant and rock and animal worlds.

Attunement to nature comes easily during the cycle of birth, when a woman's body is responding to purposes beyond her individual will. She is apt to feel more a part of nature; at the same time, nature seems to take on a more personal quality. In pregnancy, Elizabeth Green sometimes had the sensation of "being a part of the atmosphere—like a tree, rather than a thinking human being."

One summer night in my last week of pregnancy with my daughter, I piled up the pillows behind me and sat up in bed. Next to me the window was open, and the nearly-full moon shone through the walnut leaves right onto me. I put on my softest sweater and relaxed against the pillows. There were a few contractions, and in between them, the deepest peace. The face of the moon was a woman's face; I gazed at her for a long time.

Never before had I seen the moon as a living being. Perhaps it's a tendency of a mother's mind, to recognize individual beings in nature. Are we catching sight of our coming child, or projecting our own changing face? Or are we simply in a receptive state that favors seeing and attending to presences all around us?

One of the name books we pored over during pregnancy told of tribal people who sometimes name their babies after a natural event that coincides with the birth (as a California mother named her daughter "Rain"). When I first heard of the custom, it seemed a little heartless to name children after "things"; but things may become intimate companions at such a time. Receptive to our newborn's personality, we respond to everything around us in a more intimate way. (I remember being amazed at the intelligence that beamed from the eyes of our cat.) Thus the moods and "personalities" of nature weave themselves into the texture of birth and newborn days.

For many people, having a baby is the most earthy, physical experience of their lives and a vivid contrast to everything else. Those first few days of milk and diapers, I was struck with how *wet* life is. Holly Piper describes, "Meeting life in its newness, fresh, wet, yielding—"

Others feel close to nature already, with an affinity that colors their experience. "I have wonderful earthly dreams and visions after each birth," wrote Gina Jones Laughing Pony. "Each birth taught me more about my animal nature, and how to nurture." For this mother of four, a love of the natural world permeated her altered awareness in newborn time:

> I have always felt comfortable with nature and children. I've been very fortunate to witness a birth before each of my last three pregnancies.
>
> I planned my labor and deliveries as an athlete in training. I knew each time that all I wanted were soothing voices, calming eyes to gaze into, and to push that baby out like a thoroughbred horse breaking out of a starting gate. I camped in the mountains when Aura was two months old and felt like a divine mother. One who would always teach her about the earth's power and how to respect the mother earth. The energy in my body seemed so powerful. At five months old we traveled to Taos, New Mexico, we hiked to waterfalls, lived in an adobe barn and still flowed with natural surroundings. Being close to strengths made me accept my altered state of awareness quite smoothly.
>
> In 1982 I became pregnant again. I felt a calling to come East and that I did at four and a half months pregnant, once again in search of a midwife or believing I and my man could do it ourselves. December 7—birthdate of Gabrielle, had settled into a very old cabin for two weeks prior to birth. Took a walk into the night air up a wooded trail, my youngsters and my man with me. The trees had faces like in the Wizard of Oz. I kept thinking of nesting.

Labor went smoothly; once again a room full of friends breathing and panting with me. It felt like a complete circle, unity, a nice opening of my cervix for her little head to come through. I pushed and out came a smiling girl child who didn't cry but giggled and gurgled and I felt so close to the mothers in the room.

Gabrielle and I took a walk in some new fallen snow a few days later, she was so alert and I felt like a ballet, dancing with a new baby in the wilderness. We saw a small doe and I spoke to her, she listened then ran off only when a big dog came and chased her. All the ferns looked electric around the barren trees with touches of the white powder on them.

Being one who loves nature so strongly seems to have made altered experiences a super high, a union with my animal self, my newborn child very glossy and me with a feeling of mild hallucinations.

The gift of creativity became mine and my environment made life full of work but it was special, so very much I felt tuned in to all aspects of life's network . . .

Maureen experienced an expansion of awareness during the birth of her second child which allowed her to feel a wonderful closeness to nature several days later. She says:

I think my experience was due to the full opening I was able to accomplish during labor with Joshua. I was encouraged by my partner and labor coach to feel the flow of universal energy and to let it flow through me. I truly experienced that. I experienced a unity with all that exists in or out of my awareness. I was lifted from my day to day awareness of details to a wider consciousness, which included all the world around me and more than I could even consciously perceive.

I guess more simply I could state that childbirth loosened up some doors or blocks, allowing me to perceive things differently.

Three days after his birth I ventured outside and was almost overwhelmed by the beauty of the world. The lilacs were in bloom, as were the apple trees, the air was scented with the spring perfume. The black flies buzzed around a little, but did not bite me as they did everyone else!

I could hear the "music of the spheres"—a sort of cosmic concerto. I felt as light as air and although I moved slowly, it was flowingly. The air had a texture I could feel. Everything looked soft, like an impressionistic painting. There were many similarities to the psychedelic experience, sensory crossovers.

Although my new baby was upstairs, indoors, I felt totally connected with him and aware of him and knew he also felt that of me.

I felt a solitude and peacefulness. I felt singled out, quite alone, or even "different" than other people. I felt holy . . . a part of the whole picture of the world's beauty and wonder. I felt connected to the natural world.

I was filled with great joy and it seemed that the earth was rejoicing with me. I felt that the beauty, sweet smells and comforting sounds were in part for me, in celebration of the wonder of birth and my part in it. It was a gift.

Though the experience mostly ended when I came indoors, I still felt pieces of it whenever I looked or went outdoors for a few days. Since then, I feel peace more frequently and deeply. I am an important part of the universal organism and can take joy daily in that.

There was a popular poster years ago that affirmed, "You have a perfect right to be here." But I was never quite sure of belonging, until birth made me one of its channels. Then I knew myself to be a part of life's matrix. The baby at my breast seemed vast and mysterious as the planet and, as another woman put it, "I felt as if I could feed the world."

When that nurturing power flows through us, we connect with nature's mothering aspect. Feeling ourselves a part of nature, we resonate to its moods and draw on its healing vitality and restfulness.

"At the time after birth," says Gina, "I was most calm and serene watching sunsets; I had to stop everything almost daily to be with the setting brother sun."

For me it was the freshness of morning that turned my window upon leaves and sky into a view of Eden. The world shone at daybreak with a newborn's luster, and every morning seemed to be the first morning of the world. Like Dylan Thomas's recollection of childhood,

" . . . it was all
Shining, it was Adam and maiden,
The sky gathered again
And the sun grew round that very day.
So it must have been after the birth of the simple light
In the first, spinning place, the spellbound horses walking warm
Out of the whinnying green stable
On to the fields of praise."

~ ~ ~

I felt connected to all mothers
through time and space all ways.
- Lynn Amara

After childbirth, many women experience a bond with "mother" in a variety of forms: as human mothers, animal mothers, a divine being or a universal energy. Sarah Laird recalls her feelings after the birth of her daughter:

> During the first two months I was at home with her constantly. It was the coldest time of year and I was regaining my strength slowly, so I "holed up" with her and let my mother and mother-in-law and friends take care of us.
>
> I remember feeling during that time as if I was connected to all the other mothers of the world. It was something like this: all of us were trees and our roots went down into the earth and were connected together. But that is an inadequate description. It was much more spiritual than "earthy." The best I can do is to say that, in the most profound way, I felt connected to all the mothers of the world from the beginning of time.

We may feel a kinship with animal mothers as well. Carla Sunderland says:

> My cat had her first litter of kittens exactly twelve hours after I had Athena in the same bedroom, which added to my state of awareness. She seemed to be in a euphoric state also. She acted so mellow and like she felt she should be included with caring for my baby and vice versa. She moved differently, more flowing and peaceful. It was like we shared an inner knowledge of each other and our new motherhoods together.

Surprisingly, in the stories women have shared with me, they seldom mention a special attunement to their own mothers. Yet it makes sense that a feeling of being "connected to all mothers" might develop apart from the complex, ambivalent relationship with one's own mother. That feeling celebrates a woman's coming of age, and claims her new role as one of the givers of life and love. It may be a fragile identity at first, easily threatened by a mother who still sees the child in her.

But the relationship with one's mother—and father—tends to change when we become parents ourselves. We begin to see them differently, through our new experiences. This perspective may bring understanding: "A lot of things fit, make sense, that had not before, as far as past events, my own mother and father and my relationship to them."

Caring for one's baby brings up childhood memories and emotions, sometimes painful: "I was able to get in touch with anger at my own mother for instilling fears and controlling me and for not providing enough warmth and emotional nourishment." And as we struggle with the new demands of parenthood, we may come to see our parents more compassionately. Joyce Vissell writes in *Models of Love* (Ramira Publising,1986):

> While holding our first born, minutes after her birth, I resolved to be a perfect mother to her. My ideals were very high. Two days later I sat saddened. Already I had made so many mistakes. I was unable to fully manifest my high ideals. I thought of my mother and felt her beautiful, noble ideals for my brother and me, and how she too was unable to fully bring those ideals into her mothering. As I thought of her many little mistakes over the years, I suddenly felt so much compassion and admiration for how hard she tried. Then I hoped that Rami would also remember me as a mother who tried, rather than a mother who made a lot of mistakes. I was able to forgive myself and my joy in motherhood returned.

At the time of birth, some women feel a transcendent maternal presence. (Do men experience this as well?) Isabelle Kessler recalls, "At his birth I had the knowledge of `Mother.' I could feel all the Mothers who were before me and all those who would come after. Almost an energy being given to me by `Mother.' "

Karen Bard says, "Intellectually I have known that there is such a thing as that universal mother-energy. What was new was that I felt it with my whole being, not just my mind." Although her story ends with her baby's emergence, it belongs here because of what it reveals of that mysterious "mother-energy." She writes:

> This experience is entirely tied in with my labor and delivery, which I view as the most important experience of my life. Despite the pain, I think that my labor was perfect because of the beautiful interaction I had with my midwife, my husband, the hospital staff, the hospital, and the rainy spring days.
> My most clearly defined psychic experience happened right at the moment of childbirth. However, during my pregnancy I was psychically very tuned in to my birth mother, who had me when she was very young and gave me up for adoption without ever seeing me or holding me. I have never, to my knowledge, met her. I want to, but my adoption papers are lost or destroyed and it

would be very difficult to track her down. I am trying to do it with meditation and visualization, and hope that someday, if she wants (there must be the desire on both our parts), we will meet. I went to two psychic readers during my pregnancy and both told me that my birth mother was feeling a deep connection to me at that point; they also told me that she never had any more children, that she's a writer and musician and a drifter.

My psychic experience involved my mother-in-law, Hope. Hope and I have always enjoyed one another thoroughly. She had six children of her own and raised seventeen foster children as well. In the past two or three years, she has become aware that she has been "chosen" (I don't like that word but can't think of a better one) by the universal healing spirits as a person who can manifest healing energy.

She would be instructed to direct healing energies to people she knew (and, every time, was not consciously aware that they were in distress) using her pendulum. Namely, she was instructed to send colors, to bathe them in light.

I was in labor, unbeknownst to Hope. I had a two-day labor with a midwife in attendance in the birthing room of a hospital. My husband David was with me, working with me; it was very painful and very beautiful. I am a small person, gained little weight during my pregnancy. We all thought I'd have a six or seven pound baby.

For two days I had contractions, and my transition lasted for hours. The baby was turned around ("sunny-side-up") and had to be flipped over the other way before he could be delivered. It was all painful back labor. By the end of the second day, I lost hope, strength and will. I am an athlete, but my midwife Cathy said she'd never seen anyone do two days of back labor without finally giving up and having a caesarean or a forceps delivery.

Around 8:30 P.M. of day two I could push no longer. I simply lay there and screamed through the contractions. I was also getting severely dehydrated and Cathy decided to call the obstetrician she worked with to come and either perform a forceps delivery or a caesarean.

When I went into labor, I was very determined not to have a caesarean. But after two days of it, Cathy's mentioning it didn't ruffle me a bit. A caesarean sounded fine, anything sounded fine. If they said they'd have to shoot me to put me out of my misery, I would have agreed. But David knew that I wouldn't do well with a caesarean later, he knew I didn't want one in my heart of hearts. So, while we all waited for the obstetrician to arrive and the contractions were coming rapidly (I was still lying limp and screaming) he told me to try once more.

He held both my hands and I looked deeply into his eyes (something I gave up doing hours ago; I was in such a state I couldn't even look at anyone). A current of electricity shot through us both—his eyes, to me, were filled with light, and through my body I was bathed with the universal mother-force; I felt connected with every creature that has ever given birth, I was filled with energy and I pushed.

The baby's head crowned! Then Cathy and her assistant got excited, they prepared for the imminent birth because now the baby's head was out! And in the mirror, I saw myself give one more great push and my big sweet baby boy was out, and then snuggling on the belly he used to be in. The obstetrician walked in the door a minute later, a big grin on his face, relieved that he didn't have to work on me that night.

Nicholas was born May 7, 9:32 P.M. At approximately 9:25 that evening, Hope was working late (as usual) and heard her voices say, "Send yellow to Karen." It was such a powerful message that she didn't even want to take the time to get the pendulum, she just entered the healing trance-state and sent me yellow, the color of will. That yellow is the light I saw in her son's eyes when he told me to look at him and to push once more.

In a later story, we will meet another woman who felt a power flow through her when her child was born. She describes it as "the river of love I now understand to be God." Is this the same power with a different name? Karen longed to reconnect with her lost birth-mother; did her yearning create the openness to experience that presence and to feel it as a mothering energy?

The spiritual teacher known as White Eagle offers another view of these events:

> White Eagle tells us that the form of divine Mother with her angels is always present watching over the miracle of birth on the physical plane. She represents both the universal spirit of motherhood, working through the soul and body of the physical mother, and the human form of divine Mother which can be seen ministering at the birth . . .
>
> She is universal spirit which takes the human form of a mother because it is the easiest way to come very close to all her children on earth . . . Through her human-divine personality she reaches right down into the very depths of the human heart.

Beyond these many forms of mother, there is of course one more. In giving birth and caring for her child, a woman discovers new qualities of her own nature. Through these changes, she meets herself as mother.

"It Sounds Very Simple But It Changed My Life"

Can a single event completely change one's view of life? Yes—and perhaps most easily in the newborn year. The experiences we have during this time can lead to more than a temporary change in our state of mind; they can change us forever. This is most often true when we encounter something altogether new—a possibility, a glimpse of life's pattern, a way of being that we have not known before.

There are stories where a door seems to have opened, never to be closed again. There are experiences that start one moving in a different direction—to a new life-work, for example.

Pat Eisenberg is one woman who met a new perception and was radically changed by it. "I think that if you allow it to happen," says Pat, "your mind and body become more sensitive during pregnancy and after—your antennae are out, so to speak."

Here is her story, in its original form along with many of my questions:

> I am now forty-two years old, married with two sons, ten and three. I worked as an engineering draftsman and designer until my second child was born; now I illustrate college textbooks, working part time from home. I also volunteer time to La Leche League, my older son Sam's public school and my younger son Daniel's pre-school. I never volunteered time to anybody before this experience, and my friends described me as "hard to get to know" and "aloof." No longer—now I am willing to share intimate details of my life with virtual strangers. And I have a much better time.
>
> This occurred with my second baby, Daniel, born January 29, 1982, at Tucson Medical Center. I had a completely unmedicated birth and managed to refuse enema, shave, fetal monitor and IV. My husband and mother were present in the delivery room. The entire labor was about four and a half hours.
>
> When Daniel popped out and they handed him to me I had the overwhelming impression that he knew just where he was. When we went to the recovery room and Sam, who was then almost seven years old, joined us, I got a second strong impression that he and Daniel were already acquainted.

It sounds very simple but really I would say it has changed my life—I have become much looser and more intuitive since this happened, although I haven't had any more unusual experiences. I've attempted to act on ideas and impulses which I might have ignored or discounted before.

"At the time it was happening, how did you interpret your experience?"

I was amazed. But I interpreted it as a revealed truth, I guess—something which on some level I had always known to be true.

"What parts of the experience were new for you?"

It was all new. I had read a few things about reincarnation but I had never had any experience beyond the "normal."

"Parts of your after-birth experience may remind you of other times in your life. Please describe any such `echoes' that come to mind."

Once several years ago I was given some psychoactive mushrooms—I don't know what kind—which caused me to see everything as beautiful, brilliant, colorful, vivid, sharply defined. In a way, this was similar, in that I felt I was seeing "more" of this new baby.

"Had you previously heard of altered awareness or unusual states occurring after childbirth?"

No. And I probably wouldn't have believed any.

"During the pregnancy, did you have any unusual experiences, or any hints of what you experienced after the birth?"

No, but I was busy working as a civil engineering designer and hardly had time to think. And I foolishly never took time to feel.

"What was your spiritual orientation, religion or philosophy at the time of your pregnancy?"

I didn't have much. I was raised a Catholic but gave it up years ago, and my husband's family is Jewish but irreligious. I feel differently now, very spiritual but not religious.

"Did you have any difficulties with labor or delivery?"

No, it was really fun . . . I had read a great book, *Natural Childbirth* *the Swiss Way,** by Esther Marilus, which said, in effect, "Relax in labor! Just relax and your body will have this baby." By golly it worked—my body just opened up like a flower and out came Daniel.

"Have there been long-lasting changes in yourself stemming from your experience?"

GOSH YES! I have since then read more about reincarnation and I now believe that we are all little pieces of God, that we all get to be born many times till everyone on earth (and elsewhere) reaches perfection, and that when Wordsworth wrote, "Trailing clouds of glory . . . we come from Heaven which is our home" he was speaking the simple truth.

"Do you feel your experience affected your relationship with your child? Did it change your feelings about motherhood in any way?"

OH HELL YES! I always had a tendency to treat babies as PEOPLE—individuals with opinions—but I felt weird in the presence of others who saw children as clay to be molded or blank slates to be written on. Now I am sure our children choose us as parents and that our job is to gently, nonviolently, lovingly help them BE THEMSELVES—their best selves.

"Looking back on it now, what does that experience mean to you, in the frame of your whole life?"

I think it has improved my life beyond all understanding. Not that I'm perfect! I still get depressed, scream at my kids, even hit them occasionally. But I have an entirely changed perspective and a great trust in my own intuition, which as far as I can tell has always been right, even though I've spent years ignoring and denying it in favor of what I "should" do.

What could give a single impression such power to change us? Perhaps it's the state of mind that comes with transitional times. Between "sets"—when we're traveling, for instance, or convalescing—our attention floats free of the usual channels. We become more receptive, more available to new impressions. The baby's arrival brings such an interval, when new experiences and insights can deeply color the next phase of our lives.

---

* (Prentice-Hall,1979)

~   ~   ~

For Susan, the insights that came with newborn time actually shattered the basis of her life. Her story is representative of many women who become mothers without suspecting how much that experience may change them. The presence she felt during the birth of her children, and her altered awareness in the following weeks, affected her so deeply that she rebuilt her life "from ground zero" to bring it into harmony with them. She says:

> I felt holy in the weeks following my babies' births. I felt surrounded by an aura. Not because I myself was special but because the river of love that is the power I understand to be God flowed through me and my baby when she was born.
>
> I saw clearly that all other human love relationships are modeled on this purest and holiest of love known to humans. I felt mellow, beautiful and holy when she was in my arms and that incredible love pulsated around us.
>
> There is a Biblical event that relates deeply to what I experienced. It is reported that after the death of Jesus, his followers met to pray and be together in what became known as the Upper Room. Something of a very deep spiritual nature happened to them there. It became known as the Pentecost, and later writers said that these people were filled with the "Holy Spirit" which left a burning tongue of fire over their heads. The experience so affected them that they were changed and the course of their lives altered. They impressed enough other people that the whole thing we call Christianity took root from that event.
>
> I felt filled, when my first baby was born, with a holy spirit and as though a burning tongue of fire was left over my soul.
>
> Later, when I assisted a mother at a home birth with a midwife and two or three other women helpers, this feeling was intensified. It was early dawn and in the grey light among us assembled there, something extraordinary was present. I was breathless; it was as though a mighty force filled us all. It would be an accurate description of my inner state to say that a "tongue of fire" hovered over me for the next several hours, the rest of the day, as I returned to my everyday life.
>
> I knew I could *not* talk to anyone about what I experienced with my baby's birth. It was like seeing a UFO on a clear sober wide awake afternoon, when you were all alone. Whom could you possibly tell? Not only would you be disbelieved, you would be considered crazy. I had had a deep religious experience . . . I had

known God, the river of love and power I now understand to be God. Who on earth could I tell *that* to?

You asked if there have been long lasting changes in myself stemming from my experience. Yes. It changed my life entirely. The whole foundation of my adult life was shattered. I had spent years in training and education and practice as a professional (a dentist). I had a promising career with a high salary, tenure track faculty appointment, research and publications. That all fell into the background as I experienced the spiritual changes of birth and the postpartum period. I have not worked full time since and have recently quit altogether.

Unfortunately, everything I am doing now is totally nonsynergistic with anything I was doing before. Like many women of my generation (I am thirty-six), I believed, in reflection of my culture's dominant values, that the destiny of "housewife" was the fate only of those women too lazy to do "real" work, or who had failed to plan their education and lives properly. I planned to have a family—someday—worked around my career. I bought into the superwoman myth entirely.

Then I discovered that all my training as a professional and a careerist had developed skills and values that were the diametric opposite of those needed for the spiritual and emotional work of pregnancy, motherhood and nurturing of a family.

There were times when I doubted my mental stability during this transition. I wept frequently. I experienced depression as I attempted to start from ground zero to develop the needed skills and values for motherhood. I continued to work part time and enjoyed the work but was further depressed by my conflicts and compromises about child care while I worked.

I went through a great deal of culture shock and adjustment problems in working out the physical, financial and social status implications of this enormous spiritual event surrounding childbirth. I believe these problems are referred to as "postpartum depression" by the obstetric establishment. It is frequently suggested that these problems are due to "hormonal imbalances" following birth. Nothing shut me up quicker when I tried to reach out for support during this time than to have my problems referred to, however kindly, as "postpartum blues" or "hormones."

The real cause of her experience, Susan feels, is "the undeniable spiritual power of birth." She says:

It is only with the greatest effort that our culture is able to suppress our awareness of these spiritual forces. Our culture today does this primarily through our gynecologic/obstetric practices which grossly distort and disrupt the normal experience of birth. Further, most women's attempts to communicate the depth of their birth experience are denied by trivializing their messages. Women are simply viewed as excessively sentimental, and overly susceptible to the influence of their maternal hormones, anyway, following birth.

To draw an analogy, giving birth and bonding to one's child are very comparable to the adult experience of male and female falling in love. The life-altering potential of falling in love, its spiritual and emotional depths are fully accepted by our culture and thoroughly explored in movies, books, music, poetry and so on. However, the power of birth experiences is not so recognized.

There is an ironic aside I wish to make here. In the Anglican Book of Common Prayer there is a ceremony described as a "purification" for women following childbirth. It was to be performed about ten days to two weeks after childbirth. When I read this, I was struck that this was almost exactly the same period of time that my intense spiritual event lasted. It struck me too that the ceremony was exactly backwards: it wasn't I who needed to be "purified." I was in a holier state than I would ever again be in my life—it was rather the world that needed to be purified to receive me and my baby.

Well, to follow this thought a little further, male dominated religions have always had trouble with women's direct participation in spiritual experience, preferring that they go through male priests and approved formats. In an attempt to deny women this spiritual experience at birth, they inadvertently acknowledged it in a backwards sort of way with this "purification" ceremony. The fact that this period of time roughly coincides with the duration of postpartum bleeding was not lost on me, nor on the priests, in all likelihood.

I believe that our culture is so male dominated in all areas including spiritual matters, that it is virtually impossible for any of us to recognize women's experience in birth for the deep spiritual event that it can be. To do so would be to recognize women's spiritual leadership, which the major world religions have always vehemently refused to do.

A New Range Of Emotions

B y the time we are grown up and ready to have children, we've settled into a familiar range of feelings. Our emotions tend to stay within boundaries that help us define who we are. But events of the newborn year may bring us a very different experience of our emotional side.

From the beginning, pregnancy, birth and parenthood make radical changes in our self-image. Familiar boundaries shift and dissolve, creating many kinds of openness. Emotionally, we open to a whole new range of feeling, with possibilities of ecstasy at one extreme and deep emotional pain at the other. This new range of feeling includes areas of emotional obscurity where we cannot readily explain or identify the moods that take possession of us.

What we experience has much to do with what is hidden within ourselves. We'll tend to come into contact with sides of our nature not previously expressed, and with buried emotions and memories. Midwife and mother Colleen Waddell sums up the elements that make this time unique:

> The many, many changes following childbirth, requiring so much integration and reintegration. Blood loss, fluid balance changes with compensatory electrolyte and circulatory changes themselves are a lot to deal with. Recovery from exhausting labors, the stress of the whole world shifting to make a place for this new being. The growth of a family; at the same time the separation of the mother-baby unit is stressful. Also pre-birth memories of mine, my husband's, and other children. And early life memories of all of us. Things we have suppressed on this level for a long time come seeping into our consciousness with the stress and joy of this occasion.

Emotions in pregnancy and newborn time can change in many ways, but typically we can no longer rely on their old well-known patterns. This may bring a sense of being alive as never before ("I was truly a *feeling* person for the first time"), and it can also resemble being "lost at sea." Often it is the sheer intensity of emotions that carries us beyond our familiar limits.

Going beyond those boundaries can be frightening or even a part of mental breakdown. And yet it can also be the heart of ecstasy, as Pat Hunt's story reveals:

> On July 6, 1981, Selina Marjorie Hunt was born. This was my first birthing experience and was everything my husband and I could have wished for.
>
> After she was settled and I was showered, I sat out on the porch of her grandparents' home, her birthing place, and looked past the locust trees of the front lawn out over the water of Dering Harbor. Schooner Naga, our home, was out on her mooring, pointing into the southwest wind. A lovely summer/birth day.
>
> My thoughts were of my passage into motherhood and then elated feelings about having a lifetime as a woman—a thankfulness. These feelings were followed by a wave of euphoria flowing over me, wherein everything brightened to a white light and I became one with all there is. There were no boundaries of any kind.
>
> This experience lasted, I would guess, somewhere from thirty seconds to a minute; however, it had an infinite quality while it was happening. I felt touched by God. When I recall it or share it, I feel overwhelmed and my eyes fill with tears.

The words that people use to tell of their feelings in newborn time are often water-words: "great sentimental gushes took me over;" "a flood of emotions;" "swimming in bliss;" "a wave of euphoria flowed over me." These feelings have an irresistible, enfolding quality, and great power like the ocean itself. We seem to be taken over by something outside ourselves. It's deeply relaxing, when there is no need to add anything to what we feel. Thus the sense of being not-in-control can be ecstasy—life itself is moving us, and surrender is the only possible response.

Nancy met such intensity when she held her third baby and felt a deep and unexpected contact. Comparing any previous experience to this, she said, would be "like comparing the fall of a drop of water to the crash of a wave." She adds:

> This was also a PURE experience. By "pure" I mean it was untouched by human hands, if you will. No one "made" this experience happen. There were no words or ideas involved, it was just its own wondrous happening.

Intensity and purity, and the feeling that something has come to us from beyond our personal limits—with these qualities the time after birth may be "a peak experience." Linda is one who describes it in these words. Her story shows how emotional states are woven together with sensory changes and changes in body-feeling.

My son Gabriel was born at home just past midnight. I got very little sleep that night but the next morning I was wide awake, lying in bed with Gabriel and my husband, David.

I felt completely elated. I was filled with a gratefulness, first of all for my new child, but also a gratefulness to be alive and a feeling of warmth and love toward all those around me . . .

Although I had gotten very little sleep for several days, I felt energized and slept only an hour or so that first day. I felt cleansed, as though I had experienced a great emotional release. This seemed to be a peak experience of my life and I knew that I had somehow been transformed by it.

I seemed to be moving as though I was in slow motion. My touch was much more sensitive, and all of my senses heightened. These feelings lasted all week. Colors looked vibrant; everything looked alive. I had slight hallucinations—seeing a flash of something out of the corner of my eye and knowing it wasn't really there—flashes of light, images, colors.

I seemed to be seeing people more as they truly are, but viewing them with more love and compassion. It's now been over a week since I've given birth to Gabriel and I am still feeling very sensitive, although the feelings of great elation have dissipated. I haven't experienced any real depression but there have been some moments of deep sadness, when I see my five-year-old trying to cope with not being the only one any more. I still feel somehow changed, a growth that is irreversible.

Doris likens the elation she felt after childbirth to other times of great emotional and physical intensity: "A counseling session that lasted twenty-four hours—when it was over . . . A wilderness experience where I spent two weeks in minus twenty degrees snow and almost got nailed by a falling tree . . . A car accident closely missing the cliff . . . Spending many intense hours with an art project and finishing it.

"But nothing," she says, "compared to the intensity and wonderful experience of giving birth and after the birth. I felt wonderful—high—capable, strong—full of glowing energy. My partner cried. I was astonished at how painful it was and how recovered I felt." Doris emphasizes that she had expected to feel changed, "more self aware, more connected to my partner, more vulnerable, softer, more glowing, more like a perfect human after the birth or because of the intensity of the birth process. I did feel this way! I felt reborn myself and so did my partner."

Emotions during the newborn year seem more than usually responsive to the cycle of night and day. Fears may awaken at night, perhaps because they resonate with the darkness itself. Or do body cycles lower our vitality then and leave us more vulnerable? Whatever the cause, it seems clear that new mothers need company at night, and this may apply to fathers as well, as Alan's story reveals:

> I experienced a vivid and rather unpleasant "demon trying to get in me" attack during sleep on the first night following the birth of my son. I used to get these odd occurrences occasionally during my life but they ceased for the most part after I began meditating regularly six years ago. It's basically a wakening up in the middle of the night into a somewhat paralyzed frightful intense awareness of something bad trying to overcome you. Even though it's probably not the best thing to do, you struggle to resist it. During this time it's as if you're awake, you see what room you're in, the walls and doors etc., but you're not really normally awake. But you are also not asleep or dreaming.
>
> Why this should occur after the birth of my son, I don't know. I know I was extremely tired after staying up for over forty hours during my wife's labor. Perhaps it was a lowering of consciousness or natural spiritual defenses due to tiredness and lack of awareness.

This experience may be the projection of an unrecognized emotion such as fear. However, in a later section we'll see that such "invasions" are surprisingly common in newborn time, and raise other possibilities about the nature of emotional darkness.

In the days after childbirth, emotions tend to be fluid and changeable. Not only do they shift easily from one mood to another, but we can feel simultaneous joy and sadness. I remember smiling and crying at the same time, as I held my perfect baby and mourned his hard birth. The easy tears of new mothers are well known and even documented in research.

But I remember too the sudden, unprecedented tears of a new father, always an emotionally reserved man, as he struggled to write a letter about his thoughts and feelings and his one-week-old son. The only explanation he could give was: "It's all too much."

These experiences can be overwhelming in their intensity. The emotional energy to absorb them may run low, especially when one's physical energy is exhausted by broken sleep and labor's aftermath. So the moments of anxiety, fatigue and depression are not hard to understand, and yet there is another quality that often emerges—a surprising steadiness. A mother recalls:

> I am convinced that I experienced some kind of "altered state of consciousness" during the first two months after the births of my sons almost two years ago—a euphoria that enabled me to sail through caring for (including nursing) twins without ever feeling overwhelmed, depressed, anxious. I look back on those as the two best months in my life.

Overshadowed by the better-known postpartum depression, this buoyant, steady state is one of the unrecognized riches of newborn time.

~   ~   ~

As we meet unexpected emotions and unfamiliar sensations, there can be a sense of losing control. Over and over, people use the word "vulnerability" to describe their experience after childbirth.

The awareness of vulnerability, of mortality, seems to be a necessary step in growing up. Letting go the adolescent dream of control and independence, we fall from our illusions. But we fall to earth and into community with other vulnerable human beings.

"I always saw myself as being in control," says Kelly. When she experienced her lack of control in newborn time, she discovered the hidden qualities of her nature:

> Several days after Molly was born I went into states of extreme sadness. They seemed to be triggered by sunset, and would turn to dread by dark. Some of these emotions centered on Molly but mostly they were nonspecific. As soon as day returned my emotions would shift to extreme joy and feelings of protectiveness for my new baby.
>
> I also found that I had a tendency to whisper and simply couldn't speak loud. Overall there was a strong sense of vulnerability, lost at sea, I used to think of it. The emotions and sensations tapered off slowly. Now two and a half years later I could almost say I am approaching my former self, though I will never be the "same." I think the awareness of vulnerability will always be there.

Kelly believes her experiences were caused by "the enormous drop in estrogen and progesterone levels following birth, coupled with the rise in prolactin which I have been told makes you feel very `mellow' and in the present but decreases logical and arithmetic abilities." She says:

> The extreme sadness echoed a period when I stopped ovulating four years prior, and my estrogen and progesterone levels dropped so low as to be diagnosed menopausal. It is partly this that lets me know that hormones are the main factor, as the emotions preceded by months finding out about my physical condition.
>
> I definitely worried about the periods of sadness and dread and loss of logic after the birth, but they seemed balanced by the intense sensations of joy and love. I also was glad to have a chance to experience this emotion side of my nature—even hoping for it—as I had always been so rational.

The sheer intensity of my emotions, my feelings and sensations and my lack of control over these, made the experience an extended rite of passage for me. A voyage into an archetypal yin part of myself. And the "return" is not a return; I am not the same person.

"I view my life up to that point of childbirth as an extended adolescence," Kelly concludes. "I feel much more connected to the human race."

~ ~ ~

With an increased emotional openness and vulnerability we may be more affected than usual by the environment and people around us. This can create some hardship, but at the same time the openness helps us develop our capacity for a warm and giving tenderness.

Ruth Bruns experienced both sides of this emotional change. During the birth of her fourth child, time and space blended together for Ruth. Boundaries between herself and the baby seemed to dissolve. This was the beginning of a longer experience of what she calls "an intense openness." She says:

The last was the most intense birthing I have ever experienced, probably because I had no intervention. I was amazed at the intensity. It seemed the physical intensity loosened the psychic/physical web.

After the birth for approximately a month (gradually lessening) I felt an intense openness. On the physical level it seemed as vulnerability; the boundaries of my body seemed undefined. On the emotional level I felt an "open book." In going to town I felt as though anyone could poke right through me, as if my body wasn't there. This was not uncomfortable, but I felt I had to be very consciously aware. The openness made it hard to see people; television, radio, being in the car—all seemed grating to my being.

Living in rural isolation as we do, and the birthing being in winter months and having a protective partner, I had no need to extend myself and my activity outside my home. At home my energies were completely absorbed with two little ones and that seemed easier to do because of the openness I felt. It was as if my ego was outside myself and it absorbed the whole of the family and home.

My experience increased my inner tranquillity, my nurturing and bonding. My then three-year-old daughter had a great many needs for me after the birthing, and the openness I felt directly effected my ability to give from a seemingly endless source.

We may be more sensitive than usual to unspoken tensions and undercurrents. Relationships that are not easy in ordinary times can become much more stressful. One mother advises, "Do as much as you can to clarify the relationship between the parents before the baby arrives. There was far too much unsaid between my partner and me, which added tremendously to my stress level and the physical problems of the birth." Another woman found herself emotionally overloaded when her in-laws visited.

Most women who experience plummeting premenstrual moods find that they pass without leaving much residue. We recognize their cyclic nature; from their depths we can even gain useful glimpses into the neglected areas of our lives. A similar emotional low after childbirth can be much more damaging, affecting both the mother's feelings toward her baby, and her sense of self when she's most defenseless.

Lynnda Lowry has noticed a similarity between her mood after childbirth and the emotional vulnerability of premenstrual days. Some of the hormonal changes are in fact similar, especially the drop in progesterone. Lynnda enjoys her greatest self-confidence and happiness during pregnancy, when progesterone levels are highest. After each birth, she says, "I felt tied down, cried for no real reason, felt unloved, thought that everyone hated me. If I had visitors, I thought I was a big gossipper. I felt people were talking behind my back. It seemed no one understood me at all, how I was feeling."

During labor, women sometimes feel unusually open and sensitive to other people's emotions. Elizabeth Green recalls that during her long labor she seemed to be "feeling each person's emotions and judgements. Like I was in their shoes and knew what they thought about the situation." This unguarded emotional state, in which it is hard to say whose feelings are whose, appears again in the days and weeks after birth. It happened to me on Devin's third day, when he was getting hungry and I still had no milk. Each time he cried, I helplessly burst into tears. There seemed to be no psychic distance between us; his cries echoed in my body and my response was visceral.

Opened boundaries between oneself and another, and special attunement to feelings—these are basic provisions for nurturing a baby. And in the wider context of our lives, they create empathy and sometimes painful sensitivity:

> I felt a compassion toward everyone—though, at the same time, a strong desire to "protect" my son. I did not want indifferent hospital personnel even touching him. I was enormously sensitive—seeing the news or reading the newspaper could have me crying for several hours.

> I felt other people's emotions as if they were my own. At this time some Girl Scouts had been murdered in their camp. Upon hearing this, I felt grief as if these children had been my own.

This susceptibility may last a long time, and we feel its effects in many ways. Kate Mareck, for example, found that "hard music is painful. I can't relate to music of pain or anger. I hurt for people suffering so." And Jettie Regnier writes:

> One other way my awareness has changed. I am deeply agonized every time I see a parent yell at or spank a young child in a store. I could cry. I feel from the child's point of view. Children love their parents so much. How can they take the hurt?

For at least a year after Devin's birth, my eyes would fill with tears at the slightest hint of anything touching. The impact of sad stories was so heavy and long-lasting that I had to avoid reading newspapers. I recommended the same self-protection to a mother who wrote, when her baby was eleven months old:

> I have been going through a fear of the world getting so bad that I will be in a situation like that in other parts of the world—the starving and destruction going on. I'm so afraid I will be someday running for my life and I'm afraid someday I will be that mother who has to sit and watch her children slowly starve to death, knowing that there is nothing I can do about it!

We are vulnerable to such moods partly because (like other animals) we're designed to react to whatever threatens our young ones. Mother rats, for example, pay less attention than usual to many disturbances in their environment—but they are keenly alert to any change that affects their babies' safety.

We humans are at a disadvantage, with our media and our imaginations. We "normally" live bombarded by frightening information, and we maintain some emotional distance from it. In the newborn year, that distance ranges downward to zero. We may react with anxiety or feelings of helplessness as we realize we cannot guarantee our children's security. Knowing that, we become vulnerable and emotionally involved in the human family. "Stories of child abuse become more real to me," as one mother said.

Empathy and openness expose us to sorrows beyond our private experience, but they hold the community together. Sandra Ure Griffin, eight years after her first child was born, felt a lasting change within herself:

> "A heightened sense of unity with all mothers and children in the world, and with that a sense of urgency that warfare be extinguished forever. For mothers hold babes in Russia, in Nicaragua, in South Africa, in Iraq, and on and on . . ."

~   ~   ~

As they try to explain what happened to them after their baby's arrival, many people find it difficult to put their experience into words. They cannot quite identify the feelings that have overtaken them. These obscure emotions may be so unfamiliar that we lack words for them; it may also be that something more is going on than we can consciously recognize. A mother wrote:

> I felt somewhat sad and disappointed after the birth . . . I was having difficulty sorting the whole birth process out—I didn't know what hit me—I just knew it was affecting me physically, emotionally and spiritually. I felt overwhelmed with my feelings.

It's uncomfortable to be in the grip of obscure emotions, yet they can pressure us toward greater self-awareness, through dreams and daydreams, impulses and moments of sudden insight as we strive to understand them.

In Zen Buddhism, a student may be given a koan—a paradoxical riddle that can only be solved by going beyond the mind's present boundaries. The situations that arise in life can be a similar challenge. Sometimes a childbirth experience becomes a potent koan for a woman. Loaded with mysterious meaning, it compels her attention until she works through it to clarity, or time puts it in a new perspective.

Obscure emotions can bring us to a standstill. We are "hung up," obsessively trying to penetrate to the source of what we feel. In Cindy's case, she found herself obsessed with recalling the birth:

> I don't know if I had an unusual experience or just a normal response but I was amazed by how different I felt after having my daughter. It seemed to have taken many months, maybe four or five, to seem like myself again.
>
> Immediately after the birth, I was constantly going over it again and again in my mind. I kept trying to remember everything that happened and how I felt. It was an amazing feeling. It was as if I was obsessed with the birth. I should mention that I didn't have a particularly difficult or long labor.
>
> After I came home I still felt very different, strange, but it's not something I can really pinpoint. I've often said I had postpartum depression when people asked, but I'm not sure that's true. I just felt so strange. I couldn't relate it to lack of sleep because Elyse slept through the night from one month of age.
>
> Also of interest to me is that it seems that my husband and I had a hard time communicating after the baby, and I don't know if this mood I was in was a significant contributing factor to this.

An obsession with reliving the birth may come from having had a glimpse of another awareness, elusive and tantalizing like the fragment of a dream. Though Cindy says she was glad when the strange feeling that she couldn't describe finally ended, and hopes she won't experience it again with any future births, as a result of it she became very interested in pregnancy, childbirth and children. "It's the reason I finally went back to school to become a nurse and hopefully a Certified Nurse Midwife," she says. She is one of the many women who, after having a child, feel drawn to work with pregnant and birth-giving women. They may have touched a mysterious power in their birth time, and hope to stay close to it or recapture it.

Emotions that are hard to define and hard to communicate sometimes begin in pregnancy and carry over. This happened in Noelle's second pregnancy, which culminated in the premature birth of identical twin boys each weighing less than three pounds. She writes:

I have owned horses, lived alone, lived in a small commune in the city and in the country. I have lived in a twelve by fourteen foot A-frame deep in the woods without running water or indoor plumbing, attempting a self sufficient life style. I have lived with men and had a brief encounter with physical abuse by one of these men. I have been an avid handweaver and handspinner and for a brief time had my own business teaching handspinning. And so I think it's safe to say I have had a somewhat varied, maybe even unusual life to date—but no experience so profoundly unusual and deeply transforming as the birth two years ago of my twin boys.

It began with the onset of pregnancy. Even though I had been pregnant before, this pregnancy was different. I felt altered, somehow. The confusion created twenty-four-hour-a-day nausea accompanied with unrelenting fatigue. I felt I saw the world differently, tinted with a sense of rejection. There were days when I wondered how I could go on. I wished for release. My "self" as I knew it was gone and this stranger was taking my place. The stranger created feelings of separation, misery and rejection.

Finding that the pregnancy was twins seemed to intensify my feelings of disconnectedness. Immediately upon sitting up from the ultrasound table whereby twins were identified, I cried. It seemed like a long time that I cried—tears that welled up, released and kept on coming.

The second trimester (and last, since they were born at the beginning of the third trimester), physically, the fatigue "turned into" anemia, and with it rib pain which meant I couldn't even sleep on my side without pain. A tortured sense of dread stayed with me. I had little or no interest in anything, and having just moved to a new home and new state did not change the apathy which only continued to grow. My husband was busy in a new practice as an anesthesiologist and had little time; friends and family were far away.

The premature birth launched me into another segment of the whole experience. Now instead of feeling disoriented and helpless with them inside, I felt disoriented and helpless with the twins outside in a Neonatal Intensive Care Unit where they spent the next two months. They were to spend the first two weeks on life support systems and gradually come "off." My early reactions were numbness, grief, relief (the pregnancy was over?) and fear. I remember feeling very alone. Upon arriving home, one twin was on a monitor due to periods of apnea. I averaged two hours of sleep a night for six weeks, and so the sleep deprivation prolonged the altered emotional and psychological state of this total experience.

Noelle compares her state of mind with an earlier time in her life: "I experienced this disconnected feeling after having been physically abused by a boyfriend. I often felt and described `feeling insulated' or like living inside a bubble, working, moving through daily activities as though I was floating, not connected and yet acutely aware."

The resolution of such a state can be just as hard to fathom as the emotions that underlie it. We may gain only fragments of insight about the feelings and physical conditions involved. For Noelle, there was a gradual clearing:

It has been said the darkest hour is just before dawn and for me it was certainly true. Initially with Christopher, who experienced feeding problems and at six months was diagnosed as having cerebral palsy, I occasionally felt resentment along with a continual sense of confusion and isolation. But as things unfolded and I became more accepting, loving—the transformation allowed me to be a better mother, nurturer. To balance giving and receiving.

I had practiced meditation several years ago but not regularly during this pregnancy. I am now practicing meditation daily and creative visualization, and am involved in polarity therapy, chakra balancing and healing with Christopher.

It seems that Noelle solved the koan of her predicament by expanding her sense of responsibility for it. She says:

I created a clarity and growth that has for me been positive, fulfilling, and a wondrous journey for all concerned. It was as though all the cards were there, "in the deck," but shuffled, not yet in perspective. As the hand was dealt, played out, the results unfolded, allowing the light to shine, make sense of the confusion and allow a transformation that would eventually change my life entirely. The time had come to understand and know we do indeed create our own reality. The ultimate cause I now know was to learn who I am on a deeper level.

Confusing and unfamiliar emotions tend to isolate us from others. We are unable to communicate them, since they are partly hidden even from ourselves. As Noelle says, recalling the reactions of other people when she was found to be carrying twins, "Everyone around me thought it was so wonderful—all I could feel was an intense sense of dread. Further separation."

Donna Kurtz describes six months of depression after her first child's birth in similar terms of being "alone and in myself":

> My husband didn't understand what I was going through and I couldn't explain it, and I couldn't understand why he didn't understand. My thoughts were so loud inside my head, I couldn't understand why he didn't "hear." I couldn't communicate, and felt very lethargic. I thought I was cracking up! Much of my retreat was due to sleepless nights with a colicky infant. When I was thirteen we moved to a place I hated, and I retreated into myself for years. This was similar, only I didn't do it on purpose.

Such emotions alienate us from ourselves. We don't understand what has happened to us; Noelle felt as though a "stranger" had taken the place of her familiar self. We may feel ashamed of emotions that seem disproportionate to any cause that we can name.

The real cause of these emotions may be deeply buried. Sadness and anger, for example, often mask hidden fear. The emotion we feel in one situation may be displaced from another, of which we are unconsciously reminded. Even more baffling, we can feel "emotions" that are really symptoms of a physical problem. (From my days as a nurse, I recall a young man whose violent attacks of rage disappeared after a small tumor was removed from his brain.)

The experiences of newborn time are heavily loaded with past associations, many of which we do not consciously remember. Stanislav Grof, a psychotherapist, did extensive research with psychedelics in therapy before their use was outlawed. He discovered that "women reliving their birth in psychedelic sessions frequently have a simultaneous strong feeling of delivering a child. They can actually have great difficulties distinguishing whether they are being born or giving birth." Because of this connection, he views childbirth as a time of "opportunity and problem." He writes:

> The process of delivering a child seems to bring the mother close to reliving her own trauma of birth. It tends to activate . . . also all the later secondary elaborations of the birth trauma involving conflicts about sex, death, biological material, pregnancy, childbirth, and pain. Under proper circumstances, with the right understanding

and a sensitive approach, this period can be a great opportunity for deep psychological work. Conversely, if the dynamics involved is misunderstood and the mother is forced to repress the emerging material, it can result in the development of serious emotional and psychosomatic problems. In extreme cases, disturbances of this kind can reach psychotic proportions.

Things have happened to us when we were too young to understand them or to know what we felt. There may have been moments when we chose not to feel. In newborn time, when boundaries are more fluid, time itself seems to open up and we become vulnerable to our own past. As we try to understand the emotions that arise, we sometimes reclaim lost pieces of our lives.

Sunsue Fleming's experience shows how obscure emotions may clarify themselves if one can stay with the process long enough. The intensity of her first childbirth resonated to the buried memory of an earlier event. It seems that her body registered the impact first, producing a fever which allowed the memory gradually to emerge:

> The birth of my first child was very powerful. The intensity of it was quite unexpected. A week or so after the birth I started running a fever. I began re-experiencing moments from my childhood. It wasn't just a memory, it was completely there.
>
> It took several days, reliving younger and younger experiences, until I was standing in a doorway watching my parents fight. They were physically hurting each other. The intensity was too much for me at such a young age (about three), so I just turned it off. After that moment as a child, my parents would fight and I would totally pretend it didn't happen. The birth triggered that moment for me. After I relived that moment, my fever broke. I felt as though the birth process for me was finally over.

Even a very young child can "decide" to close off a part of her life. Monica Miller Soper is another woman who made the same unconscious choice to evade painful emotions. Again, in the special conditions of the newborn year, those self-defensive inner walls came down—with results that were nearly disastrous.

"I'll start with a little teen-age background," Monica writes. "With my first love affair I became pregnant at fifteen. I entered a home for unwed mothers at seven months pregnant. No other options ever entered my mind than giving up my child. Because of intense denial mechanisms I didn't fully participate in what therapy was available and had no idea of the impact this would have on my life. I didn't grieve."

Monica has been married now for nine years and has a five-year-old daughter. "Mothering has been one of the most rewarding times of my life," she says. Shortly after this daughter's birth, Monica's suppressed emotions came out with uncontrollable force and carried her into a psychotic state. The first sign of trouble appeared during the pregnancy. "When I was in my eighth month," she recalls, "I began overeating. I'd wake in the middle of the night, jump up and eat a banana practically in my sleep. I believe now that as I was approaching my due date I was using food to stuff down feelings that were beginning to surface."

I knew I'd need time to deal with problems after our baby was born so I stated no visitors would be welcome (meaning out-of-town relatives) for at least one month.

The birth was easy, quick and joyous, a natural birth in the hospital with a midwife. I laughed during labor and our baby would cork-screw down. It was wondrous. I'd never been happier. She was a beautiful miracle; I felt proud of myself and my child.

One month after childbirth, my in-laws arrived for a two week visit. I pushed myself too much. There was not clear communication between myself, my husband and his parents. I felt supersensitive to unsaid communications. All of my buttons for over-performing were punched. I began not sleeping well between nursings at night and missing my daytime naps because of extra activities and lack of peace and quiet. I had no network of friends in the town we were living in—we'd moved there five months earlier. The couple of friends I knew were out of town.

One week after my in-laws arrived, things began being really wacky. I was crying a lot. Not sleeping. So, my husband and I sent his folks off on a day trip so I could sleep. I darkened our room, put cotton in my ears to try to dull my super-sensitive senses. My daughter was in bed with me for ease of nursing.

Suddenly I perceived Alisha wasn't breathing. I screamed out for Paul. He was not supportive. I insisted we take her to the hospital to be checked. We did; she was fine.

I was terrified of losing another child. While at the hospital I was given a mild dose of a sedative to help me sleep. We returned home and I was relaxing, until my in-laws returned.

I was seeing reality through fears. Fears of loss, grief welled up in me. It was now hitting me what I had given up with the adoption of my firstborn daughter. I became hysterical when my confused husband seemed to not be there for me. I insisted we return to the hospital. At this point my nerves were raw, my senses changed and a lifetime of unfelt feelings were crashing in through the cracks of my sleepless existence.

I listened to the nurses and doctors who said it would be best for me to stay the night and send my one-month-old home with her daddy and formula. My strength was weakened by my confusing state. When I realized I was in a hospital without my baby, I left barefoot and hitch-hiked home at midnight to my baby.

I knew at this point I needed help. Unfortunately the help I received was running against the grain of my soul. The social worker I saw put me on Thorazine. It was awful needing help—needing to be comforted, reassured, listened to—and receiving drugs.

Every detail in my environment became a symbol. I would interpret it in a non-ordinary fashion. Colors were highly significant; white, purple and pink were my choices of colors to be wearing, and also for my daughter. I registered the fear of others as they reacted to my perceptions. I realize now that I seemed delusional with my hallucinations. It was very difficult.

My mother flew up to try to help. I needed a woman, I needed my mother. Yet, she was at a loss, and I was lost. After four days at home on Thorazine I checked into the psychiatric ward. I knew if I didn't come back soon I never would. My despair was so great, my pain so deep, with waning strength I agreed to take Haldol and Cogentin, and sent my baby home to be cared for at night by my husband and my mother.

After one night of sleep (broken, but sleep) I re-entered the ordinary world. I left behind the odd symbols, sensations and visions. I kept the memories of being one with a candle flame—one with God flowing in the eternity of River Time. When I awoke in the psych ward, I felt I had had a great opportunity for spiritual growth, and it was mishandled. I missed my "enlightened state" but was glad to "be back."

Over the past five years I have explored the reality-based fears and grief and my previously unfelt feelings. Individual, group and couple counseling with sensitive therapists has been my daily bread.

I am working on recognizing my feelings and experiencing them as they come up. I now reach into each moment as fully as I can, releasing my past as a battered child, incest survivor and grief-stricken teenage unwed mother.

With that startling last line, we realize that the process of closing off the awareness of her feelings must have begun very early for Monica.

Boundaries are opened in newborn time—and so are the inner barriers we have made to keep from knowing our own pain. From inside and out, much is coming into consciousness. If we can absorb it, self-knowledge deepens and our lives are enriched. If it rushes in too fast, the rational mind can lose control, and we no longer know how to interpret what is happening in and around us. When the confusion of inner and outer realities is extreme, we become psychotic.

This is not a win-or-lose situation. Being crazy for a while can still bring self-knowledge, as it did in Monica's case. But the psychotic state is extremely dangerous for mother and baby. Mothers can harm their children while acting out delusions. Some of their sad stories have been publicized in recent articles and books such as *The New Mother Syndrome: Coping with Postpartum Stress and Depression* (Simon & Schuster,1985) by Carol Dix. One woman, for example, killed her infant son in the belief that her husband would resurrect him and reveal himself as a savior.

We are not talking about airy fantasies that you can talk a person out of believing. For those who haven't "been there," it's hard to understand the compelling reality of such delusions. One woman has described it this way:

> There was never a moment when I looked at myself clearly and saw anything odd about what was happening. Everything and everyone seemed to be affirming me all the time. Even when they told me I wasn't making sense, I heard it as a signal of agreement. I was trying to do my part as I understood it, but it was all based on wrong assumptions. You can't will to be sane, or always know the difference between hallucination and reality. What was affecting me had more energy and power than the rational mind.

Monica was fortunate; she entered a psychotic state and came out again unharmed. She was fortunate in realizing that she needed help, and fortunate in her response to the second round of medications. She quickly rejoined the "ordinary world" of shared reality, which is where she needed to be to care for her baby. (If we have the luxury of time, I think a slower, protected passage through that inner world can make better use of its opportunities for insight and healing.)

Monica was fortunate too that the symptoms of her distress were out in the open and dramatic enough to be obvious to those around her. The most dangerous situation arises when a woman is able to hide her irrational thinking under a surface of normal actions. Mothers have sometimes harmed their babies or themselves after giving very little indication of their inner chaos. So we need to be aware, and to have partners who are aware, of the full range of possibilities in the newborn year. We need to know both the dangers and the beauty of opening up hidden parts of the psyche. As she looks back now upon her breakdown/breakthrough, Monica says, "It was an awakening. A spiritual door opening for me. It was one of the most impactful experiences of my life."

Creativity And Exalation

*T*he sensitivity and altered awareness that many parents experience in the newborn year can bring a surge of creativity. Deeper levels of the mind seem more accessible than usual, yielding a flow of new ideas and imagery. For those who are already writers, musicians and artists, it can be an exciting period. The same sensitivity may awaken the poet and artist within each one of us, surprising us with our own creative power.

Heightened sensory awareness contributes to the creative potential of this time, and so does the satisfaction we feel in being able to nurture a new life. Sallie Brutto lived in the Roman countryside with her husband, her little girl and a new baby. Later, she wrote about that lovely time:

> The stems of wild iris that had sometimes come along on the breakfast tray, I went out now and pulled them myself from under the syringa bushes along the *viale*. I heard the cool, cork-drawing sound as the sheath gave up its ivory-ended stalk. I smelled the earth and the leaf-mold and the drifting wood-smoke from the house of the farmer over the hill. I heard the carts rumbling by on the road to market, the jingling of harness bells, the snapping of whips. I saw the morning light enlarge and change and the westward-reaching shadows shorten in the courtyard.
>
> This is supposed to be adversity, I would reflect gloatingly, being "stuck without a maid," and I would go back into the big morning-bright kitchen with my hands full of blue flags, and the muffins would be just browning in the portable oven and the coffee would be perking. And upstairs my new and lovely baby would be stirring again and when I thought of her my breasts would tingle sharply with the in-rushing of sustenance, and I would walk way up above the tiles in my vanity and joy for all the things I could do and make and experience and provide.

Such is the mood that sometimes comes in newborn time: an exultant sense of capability, and keen appreciation of the beauty and vitality around us. In this mood, unsuspected abilities may suddenly blossom.

Ideala Colgate describes how she started to read scripture when her baby was two or three months old, "and for the first time the Bible was an open book." This confident state, wherein the meaning of things seems to become clear, is fertile ground for creation.

Sometimes a particular talent is enlivened by the flow of fresh energy. Patricia, an adoptive mother, noticed "lots more creative ideas, and much less sleep required. And strong awareness of my singing ability."

Holly Piper also found that the quickening of creativity was accompanied by changes in her sleeping pattern. "Sleep has become erratic—sometimes I'm very charged with energy and ideas and I'll stay awake all night working on things, not even aware that the night has passed until I hear the roosters crowing and see the sun coming up." In the year after her child was born, Holly experienced a flowering of abilities:

> Something kind of transformational was happening to me. I have always enjoyed taking art and craft classes but I always felt like I was "learning" something that other people had as an inner thing. For example, in a particular weaving class, we were asked to keep a journal. I felt pretty intimidated by a whole book full of blank pages that was up to me to fill up. I really struggled with it—clipping things from magazines that "inspired" me etc. I marveled at the people who seemed to write or draw in it freely.
>
> A few months after Emma's birth I started waking at nights to record some of the images I was having in my head. Sometimes I would just sit back in the dark and watch them play through my head as if they were on film. It was almost visionary—beautiful sculptural forms and textures—things were coming out and I never dreamed they were inside of me—it was almost like they came through me but weren't of me. They have given me the strength or courage to want to pursue that avenue for awhile—maybe finish my degree in art, only because they were so strong. It's funny because it's stuff I never considered before. I would see images and I would think, "But I don't know how to connect the materials," but they would dance through my head for my pleasure or inspiration or something . . .

After my son's birth, I felt I had tapped into an infinite supply of creativity. Never had I known such delight in savoring my world, or such an effortless flow of ideas. If I had been able to play with them all day, I still could not have used all the designs and plans that bubbled up in me. When I remember how fully I enjoyed taking photographs, capturing bits of poetry and coloring birth announcements, I know this was the one time in my life when I lived as an artist, connected to the source within me.

Something was missing, however—though I didn't miss it then. I had no critical judgement, no second glance. Every idea seemed like a good idea. The results were sometimes embarrassing (to my later self), and I was lucky that my baby's needs and my own physical weakness kept me from carrying out more of them.

It can indeed be difficult to use the creative power of newborn time. Alicia describes her frustration at not knowing how to use its "raw potential" and not having the energy to explore the possibilities. Another woman adds, "Giving birth definitely opened floodgates of creative ideas, but much of my actual energy is drained off by childcare."

There is a mood, however, where we seem to be living in the very heart of creativity, and all our activities are illuminated from within us. Here is how Jann Light describes it:

> I've oscillated between feeling that my memories of Adam's birth and afterward were fuzzy and that nothing important had happened, to thinking that what I experienced was incredibly profound and of use to every person on earth. I've somewhat settled to a position midway. It has been two years since Adam's birth but although the time may have made my memory a little fuzzy it also has allowed some maturing perspective to develop.
>
> The most obvious and constant feeling of the months after September 6, 1982, the day Adam was born, is the sense of total euphoria and exhilaration. I was happy, but happy isn't a complete enough description. Euphoric is better because it was like being elevated to a higher plane of existence. The world was lit with a golden light, we moved on clouds (as opposed to through them like we do now sometimes!). The world was Adam, myself and Rick sometimes (Rick is my husband and Adam's father) and nothing that wasn't Golden Joy.
>
> Often for a few minutes during meditation I will feel euphoric, exhilarated or as if I have limitless awareness. But not for a period of weeks or months such as this. My awareness of—HIGHER LEVELS—(I can't find a good way to describe this) was very acute. I'm tempted to say my awareness was heightened in general, but there is an important clarification to make here. I was totally unaware that there was trouble, suffering, doubts and wars in the universe. The Reason for existence was totally clear to me—we are here to expand Joy. The existence of a Supreme Being (or Beings as I began to suspect) was perfectly clear. My job here on earth was definite, comfortable and perfect: to be a mother. So, awareness of what I'll call "higher levels of life" was acute, open, very expanded. But I had forgotten or left behind the "world" which we hear about on the *CBS Evening News*.
>
> One of the first specific experiences I had after Adam was born was that of the acceleration of Time. It was as if, for twenty-nine years, it had made very little difference which direction I was

going or which path I took—I always would have time to get back to the main road. But a day or two after the birth I had the distinct feeling I was on the other side of the hill now and the train was headed Down and there were no brakes.

Having had a couple of years to live with this feeling I have realized two things. Before Adam I had no "measuring stick," if you will, to see how fast time was going. Now that he is living with me I have a constant reminder of how much growth can be accomplished in a small amount of time. Two years had not seemed like a great deal of time three years ago. Now I see that in two years a person has grown from a newborn entity to a child of tremendous activity, intelligence, personality and dynamism. From total potentiality to a grand Presence with lots of potential. I have since realized as well that this acceleration I felt was a real experience of having found my correct Path of Evolution in this life and being able to progress at a much faster rate.

Jann became aware of the creative power of her work as a mother:

Another experience I had for several months is the knowledge that I was doing a service to Humanity by mothering my child. My work was of vital importance to the Earth, the Universe, and the race of Humans we are part of. An extension of this feeling was that: the way in which I mothered my child had a direct and powerful influence on all the people I encountered. I remember several specific incidents of feeling like this while being "out and about" with Adam as a tiny baby. On walks, in a park, on a bus, in a grocery, I couldn't have counted the people who were obviously elevated—in happiness or joy of course—by speaking to us or just seeing us. I had never before in my life felt quite that much power in my sphere of influence, but of course I had never had a sphere of influence generated by me and someone else. It was in actuality *our* sphere of influence. All the same, the number of smiles I saw spontaneously spread on people's faces was a proof to me that my work and life with Adam was an uplifting factor in the world.

~   ~   ~

Exaltation and heightened energy can blend into the borderland of insanity. We are not well equipped to handle long periods of exhilaration and heightened awareness; the mind reacts to this "eustress" in strange ways. As we shall see in a later chapter, exaltation can veer into mania, and creative energy can be hijacked by delusions.

For Mary Eileen, experiences in the newborn year were both "a sacred event" and a breakdown. Her exalted mood took her to the edge of insanity, but ultimately to a balance where creativity and daily life enrich each other. We've focused on the way the changing awareness of newborn time can stimulate creativity; another perspective emerges from Mary Eileen's story. Creativity can be a safety valve, channeling high energy into expression. "Although I was questioning my mental stability," she says, "I'm glad I had spirituality to `fall back on,' and my own musical creativity aided my coping mechanisms." Mary Eileen writes:

> After the birth of my first child, my husband and I returned home from the hospital with our little "chickie." As Moira was born on the day after Easter that year, the significance of Springtime presented itself most solemnly and personally! The weeks which followed were exhilarated with a spiritual energy.
>
> I nursed Moira for a year, and on her first birthday conceived our second child. Around this time, I started back to work as a Church organist—a new field of specialization which worked in extremely well with full-time mothering.
>
> In the months that followed Elena's birth, our family adjusted in varying degrees to the reality of "two under two." We had visitors frequently and housework became secondary to other basic needs! Losing a finer touch on the housework scale was parallel with a similar loss-of-touch with the reality of current events.
>
> In May, I began to feel that kind of "enlightenment" which comes at an extended period of sleep loss. Fatigue in my limbs was felt, and I suppose it was all of this, combined with continued weekend organ-playing, bringing Elena to Church with me, nursing between the "Alleluia" and the "Offertory" (our babysitter walked the baby while I was playing)—breakdown time!
>
> Mid-month, I began to focus more and more religious significance to simple events. This would not have been so heightened, perhaps, if my job did not require such a dedication or direction. Nonetheless, my vocation is just that. The most significant of these events were the Easter-Resurrection season, the month of the Blessed Mother, and a recalling of an actual miraculous healing in my own life.
>
> Briefly, when I was fourteen years old, I had an appendectomy. Following the operation, a tumor was found to be present within the appendix. Instead of the normal short hospital stay, I was in the hospital for two weeks and discharged under close supervision. Due to the location of the tumor, in an "unnecessary" organ, and because of the healing which did take place, my story was presented to the Archbishop as a possible miracle attributable to a saint at that time in consideration for the final stages of canonization, where miracles must be documented to the candidate.

Following my recuperation, I was asked by a priest friend to visit the shrine where the saint's body is entombed. At fourteen years old, without access to transportation, one excuse after another (including my own disbelief) prevented me from following through on these instructions. And the years rolled by . . .

I recalled this long-overdue "calling" during May, 1985. "No excuses now . . ." On the morning of my decision to visit, I composed a hymn to the Blessed Mother incorporating both Gabriel's "annunciation" to Her and Her "magnificat" response. When my husband awoke that morning, I asked him to take me to the shrine—a sense of urgency so basic in the list of psychotic/neurotic symptoms.

We went, and the experience was most revealing. I was drawn to the altar where the saint's body resides, as if by an inner "rope" attached to my solar plexus. When we arrived, a prayer service was going on, and the priest invited the congregation to revere a relic at the altar.

My emotions welled up to tears as the passage of time in healing revealed itself to my now-matured, now-ready mind. I knelt with the other worshippers, holding Elena (asleep through the whole thing), kissed the relic, and my husband and I both heard the priest utter "something unintelligible" (as my husband phrased it)—although I could pick out certain Latin words in his chant. A woman kneeling next to me quieted me, comforting, "Watch yourself. And watch the baby. And try not to cry."

When later questioned, the priest who chanted the Latin I heard could not remember doing it. (I wanted to know what prayer it was.) He had no recollection of saying anything in Latin, and the usual prayers for revering a relic did not include any Latin! But my husband heard it, and I knew *he* wasn't crazy!

I concluded that it was God's way of telling me that a healing had taken place, even through my unbelief. And that was a spiritual awakening-healing-maturing in itself. It was an adult-parent passage, a confirmation of personal wholeness, and a rededication to my integrated lifestyle—motherhood and musicianship combined, for example. A sense of purpose realized. I've been blessed, a journey of a shaman! The meaning of sacredness—sweetness.

The heightened awareness continued following my visit to the shrine, but with a more internalized message of protection, grace, and daily life's sacredness. The message was, basically, "You can see all of this beauty and holiness without really trying. It's all right here, accessible." I found that it was probably better to keep much of the experience to myself — thereby equipping me with an inner source of mystery and beauty from which I could draw practically—a source of strength.

Edges

B y the time a woman has shared her body with another being for nine months, seeing it so altered and finally opening to birth, she may feel as if erased all around the edges. "I see birth and death as similar," a mother says, "taking us to the edge, taking us out of our normal existence."

One night when baby Devin was newborn, as I lay in the darkened bedroom aware of him in his crib not far away, a sudden feeling of unreality about our now-separate existence sent me falling into the blackness between the stars. I felt my "personality" scattered as if shaken from a salt-shaker out into space. It was a glimpse of annihilation that quickly passed, but some people fall into it and can't easily get out again.

There is something about this transitional time that can loosen our sense of reality. One mother describes it as a lowering of the individual's defenses: "I felt stripped of my day-to-day self," she says. "I felt open and vulnerable beyond anything I'd ever known before."

Vulnerability is a normal part of the newborn year. But it can go much further, turning into an emotional desert where a woman feels isolated, alienated from herself and others and from the baby as well. This is one form of the syndrome known as postpartum depression.

On the flip side of depression we may experience an overwhelming excitement that can also steer us out of control. Or our altered sensory perceptions can become full-blown hallucinations. It seems there are limits to our adaptability—edges we don't know about until we overbalance from too much stress, too great a change in some part of our being—and the familiar self is lost.

In this chapter we'll explore these edges with four women, each of whom experienced profoundly altered states following the birth of her first child. Two of these women suffered from depression, one became manic and one went through a prolonged period of hallucinations. To understand them better, we'll also look at their lives before and after the emotional crisis.

~   ~   ~

Anita: "This State Controlled Me"

I gave birth to a beautiful daughter in September 1984 in a hospital setting, medicated, against my and my husband's wishes. The birth was traumatic for both Jamie and me, and both my husband and I have suffered from guilt and frustration, anger and resentment toward the doctor since.

After Jamie's birth I experienced many "hallucinations," highs and lows, and in trying to fight all these emotional experiences, wound up hospitalized for depression when Jamie was seven months old. I hope that by sharing my experiences and learning about others', I can work through this and finally resolve it.

I am thirty-one, home for the first time with a ten-month-old child, married and trying to live creatively on one salary. We hope to raise our only child to fulfill herself spiritually, mentally and physically. I have a B.A. in Literature and studied metaphysics extensively for five years, including yoga, but have neglected that area of my interests for some time. I do crafts, mostly original quilts, and some dressmaking.

I've been told I am perceptive, and feel my intuition and psyche were well-developed. I believe strongly in reincarnation, soul-growth and life-for-a-purpose. My conflicts are between dealing with a material world and maintaining psychic awareness.

Before my husband Barry and I met, I knew I was waiting for him and we recognized each other and loved each other very quickly. Barry has never studied any of the metaphysical sciences so it was all quite new and unnerving to him.

Five weeks after we were married, Barry had a near-fatal heart attack and briefly lost consciousness. The feelings I'd had of our destiny together were strongly tested. It took a great deal of courage to have a child and get on with life in general. I just had to give up trying to hold on to thoughts about security when Barry was so ill, and know I had strengths that I wasn't yet aware of.

My husband had strong contact with our daughter before conception, during our pregnancy, at birth, and since. My only contact was through shared dreams he and I had several times during the pregnancy. We would actually have the same dreams the same nights, although because of different psyches, not all elements were identical. This occurred only during our pregnancy, and not before or since. Also, Barry knew Jamie, knew her sex, saw her face, and loved her before her birth. She and I have only since met. My feelings about the prospect of having the baby and becoming a mother—I was excited and anticipated the chance to nurture and love a new person.

Anita's labor was thirty hours long, and complicated by "failure to progress." She writes:

My doctor never showed up and a young resident delivered my child. Because of this, my anxiety and fear were much greater than I had hoped. I was very angry at the way we were "handled," and being given medication against my wishes. My anger and fear over-rode my other emotions. (Not a happy way to birth a baby!)

I was given morphine so I could "rest" during active labor by a tired doctor who needed to sleep. I didn't rest, but entered a state of hallucinations that altered my whole concept of my daughter's birth and our postpartum period. I felt physically detached, as if I were watching the whole experience from outside my body.

During the morphine-induced state, I started believing I was in Hell, suffering terribly, and not knowing why. I forgot I was in labor and about the child, and was fighting demons. I saw them, felt their presence, and heard them. Because of my lack of physical involvement in my labor, it progressed slowly and erratically. I was given pitocin by IV to speed things up, but remained disassociated, right through a forceps delivery. My child, who before my labor felt like a familiar soul whom I couldn't wait to meet, now seemed to be a stranger.

Although we nursed and shared a room, the demons stayed too and I had terrible nightmares and headaches the two nights in the hospital. At home, during night feedings, I saw them, heard them, and felt presences all around us. I felt as if a battle were going on for my daughter's spirit, and I had to fight to protect her.

Like many women who experience depression, Anita was isolated, lacking a supporting network of friends and family:

I had no help at home, no support people, my husband had to work. Although we had no other responsibilities, we were inexperienced with the baby and felt very alone.

Our daughter had colic, so I was up most nights with her, and each night it seemed I entered this altered state where all levels of time and space occurred simultaneously, and I found it difficult to remember where and when I was actually living. Our bonding was slow to develop and during my depression I gave very little of myself to my daughter, other than physical care.

This state was different from others I had voluntarily sought before, through meditation and yoga, in that it controlled me. Eventually I stopped being able to sleep and became exhausted and depressed. I was hospitalized for depression for two and a half weeks, and on an anti-depressant I can now sleep well. My dreams are very lucid and prophetic, a change from before my pregnancy.

A few months after the hospitalization, Anita was able to reflect upon the significance of her experiences, including the hallucinations which lasted for three months following Jamie's birth:

> My daughter and I are very close psychically, and I do believe that my experience was real, and continues to be purposeful. It seems she had her own demons to fight, and needed my help, and we are now, finally, responding more to the physical world together. She has become a very joyful little person, although occasionally I still feel that state, when I am very tired, or when she has been ill. Although I didn't fully experience her birth, we are progressing beautifully now, and I am loving her with the real me!

Anita feels that the circumstances of Jamie's birth, and especially the terrifying effects of medication, triggered her tailspin into depression. But in keeping with her spiritual beliefs, she finds deeper reasons for the situation. "I needed to take a good look at who I was and what that means in terms of parenting. And I had become lazy spiritually and didn't have the psychic strength to deal with my daughter's birth the way I wanted to."

A continuing correspondence reveals more of Anita's journey through the process of healing. "Thank you for sharing your experience," she wrote. "It's given me the courage to share some more thoughts with you; a faith realization I've come to in the past few months through counseling."

> I believe there is an influx of truly developed souls into the world right now, our children, and that some of the experiences we've had birthing them are a result of long-awaited karmic "needs" being fulfilled.
>
> As I mentioned before, our daughter Jamie had colic. She did not suffer from "gas pains" or any of the other simple explanations I'd read about. It was as if, each day, she was interacting for a period with outside energies which she was not equipped, physically, to handle because of her young age. We tried massage, music, chanting, and each would bring comfort for just a little while. She seemed to be having out-of-body experiences which short-circuited her immature nervous system. Being unable to help her was very painful for us.
>
> Later, when Jamie became more vocal, her "language" sounded like mantras or Indian chant-songs, and was beautiful to hear. She has always seemed wonderfully wise and aware, and I have felt from time to time that she understands much more about me and my husband than her age should allow.
>
> We have wondered if we are up to the task of raising Jamie well, and find it very challenging to keep up with her need for information about the world. How do we, as parents, know that we are relating on all levels, telepathically as well as emotionally to our

children? For us, it is faith that Jamie chose us as her parents so that we all can learn together. She has given us a new hope for the world's future, which before her birth seemed poisoned and corrupt. The "demons" we fought in her early days will probably have to be faced again in her life. I pray we've helped her find courage.

I believe our children are special, and this may be part of the reason for the unusual experiences we had at their birth.

Anita speaks of regaining her sense of spiritual identity and growth as a result of the crisis she has been through:

> Through counselling, I am trying to resolve the trauma and pain of the experience and define the areas of my soul that need a good housecleaning. I have regained my spiritual goals and reawakened to my inner self.
>
> I have found that in learning to love Jamie the way she *needs* to be loved, I am letting go of most of my ideas of how love feels. It flows so smoothly when I let her be the child-person she is—and I'm surprised to find myself loving other people's children too, seeing right past the runny noses and "brattiness" that got in the way before I became a mother. This is what evolution for me has been, in this experience and so far.

~ ~ ~

Ephy: "I'd Given Up . . . Me"

Ephy Costas Holly came to motherhood as an idealistic, ambitious young woman of extraordinary energy despite her history of mild multiple sclerosis. She expected to fit mothering into a life of full-time work, dance and graduate school. But the reality proved quite different, and after several months of coping with the new physical and emotional demands, Ephy was suffering a painful sense of self-loss:

> I am the first child of Greek parents. Both parents came to the United States. I spoke only Greek in first grade. The teacher felt I'd never learn English and suggested to my folks that I be institutionalized because of this "unsolvable" problem. My father was a barber at the closest institution for the mentally retarded and was appalled at the suggestion! He told the teacher to give me six months and I'd learn. Sure enough. Here I am today.
>
> My years growing up were quiet. I was shy. My mother went to work when I was ten. I remember coming home and hiding in the pantry eating peanut butter and crackers until she got home half an

hour later. Consequently, I'm overweight. Always have been, probably will be.

I danced from age twenty-four to thirty-one. I was very involved, became part of a small dance company whose emphasis was Martha Graham technique. While all this was happening I was thinner, and working full time as an instructor of vocational skills.

Then my husband and I decided it was time for family. So I slowed down my pace, danced less, became pregnant, miscarried. I decided in order to get pregnant I'd have to change my lifestyle drastically because I'm high-strung and sort of a Type-A personality. So I quit the dance company and dance, joined a non-pro dance-aerobics class and started walking. At the same time all this was happening I was accepted in graduate school. I took classes on a part-time basis.

I became pregnant the summer of 1983 and continued to take courses and work till December. I took a leave from teaching in mid-January. My goal was to return to work full-time in September, resume grad school, start dancing and be a Mother. I was so idealistic. I never once concerned myself about the future. I loved the pregnancy; I felt whole, loved, complete.

After Ephy's water broke, labor was induced and seems to have gone smoothly. She was given Demerol forty-five minutes before Ana was born. "Because my mother gave me horror stories I expected 'deathening' pain," she says. "It was not that way at all. It was physically harder than aerobics though!" But Ephy's transition to motherhood was beset by frustrating events:

For the first five days I stayed in the hospital because my daughter was jaundiced. I was ready to leave the next day so I was rather annoyed and cried a lot. When I got home I started having trouble nursing my baby. She'd gotten used to bottles of water between nursings (against my and the doctor's wishes) so she didn't want to attach. I called La Leche League and got lots of advice. A week later we were becoming accustomed to nursing.

Then the trouble began. Just as my daughter and I were becoming "the happy nursing couple" my mother started falling apart. She said I was starving the baby and kept trying to interfere. Finally when I could stand it no longer I asked her to either comply with my mothering or leave. She threw a tantrum, threw dishes around in the kitchen, whined, ran out of the house and then sheepishly came back in only to stand over me to intimidate me into stopping. I put up with that twice. Then I'd nurse Ana in the bedroom with the door closed.

What agony! What pain! My thoughts in my journal: "I thought that Ana's birth would make my relationship with Mom better.

Instead it's worse. I find I don't want her near Ana. I want to run away, far away."

Cut off from everything that had defined her identity before Ana's birth, and lacking the support she needed in her new role, Ephy began to register physical and emotional effects of stress and loss:

The most peculiar experience happened on the second day I was home (Ana was one week old). I was nursing her on the couch and when I looked up everything seemed to have a vertical venetian blind effect. I felt as if I couldn't focus and got really concerned. I have multiple sclerosis, and I panicked because I thought I was having vision problems. I went right to bed and stayed there the rest of the day and the "venetian blind effect" went away.

During the first five months of Ana's life I so missed my dad (who'd died four years earlier). I wished he'd see her. I kept feeling like he could see her and that made her his grand-daughter. I'd bring her to the cemetery and feel like he'd seen her there but I wasn't sure. I felt very raw and vulnerable emotionally during the period after childbirth. And TIRED . . . would I ever rest enough???

In August about five and a half months after the birth I experienced an extreme depression. The colors were grays and everything seemed so hopeless. I was so UNWELL emotionally. I questioned my very existence and my mothering, the fact that I'd given up my career, grad school, me. I was in pain. I went to therapy because all I'd do is cry. Am presently still in therapy; the shades of gray passed after two months.

Motherhood has been unlike any job, test, project, dance I've ever undertaken. What a change for me. I'm still adjusting but only after ongoing therapy, re-evaluation of goals, etc. I'm now becoming comfortable with part-time graduate school, part-time work two and a half days a week and full mothering, no more dance, just walks and gardening. I'm liking it better and better every day. There's room in life for everything.

Fifteen months after the birth, Ephy reflected on the changes in herself:

My experience slowed me down, put things into perspective in my life. I've slowed my pace; I'm putting less pressure on myself. I'm seeing things more realistically, not idealistically. We're coming to terms with wanting another baby. This time it'll be my way. I'll nurse totally, will have no company at home for two weeks and will hire my neighbor's daughter to come in once a day to straighten up and take Ana for a walk or play with her in the house. The time for all this to occur will eventually take place. We'll play it by ear . . . I've gained a lot of strength by this whole experience.

Nine months later, Ephy's second daughter was born. When little Sophia was fifteen months old, Ephy wrote again. "Our experiences with her have been positive," she said. "I, on the other hand, still grapple with motherhood . . . but we survive. It is very difficult trying to get TIME to study, type and think beyond the realm of diapers, nursing, playgroup, nursery school and general survival."

Marriage is sometimes described as a process of continual adjustment that sandpapers our rough edges until we can live in harmony. Ephy's story reminds us that parenthood is a similar process, with the daily friction of needs and personalities in different stages of life. If we're not pulverized by it, perhaps we're smoothed until we fit our places gracefully . . . pebbles on the cosmic beach.

~   ~   ~

Betsy: Energy Out Of Control

What happens when the high energy of newborn time continues to mount? It can spiral into a "positive feedback loop." The more energy you have, the less you sleep. The less you sleep, the more excited you feel— believing that you've achieved a superhuman level of functioning. Meanwhile the subconscious mind is opening and pouring more energy into the system, along with insights that seem extraordinary. You become still more excited, sleep even less—and the energy spins out of control.

Betsy entered this spiral soon after her first child was born. Unfortunately neither she nor her attendants recognized what was happening, and the process continued into a manic state.

"It is my feeling that women should be made more aware of what to expect when giving birth," Betsy says. "I was shocked at what happened to me immediately after having given birth to my son. No one uttered a single word about the possibility that this might happen to ME! I am very bitter towards my obstetrician and the nurses who said they knew nothing of what was going on with me."

Betsy had previously suffered mental derailments related to drug use. Other factors made her especially vulnerable in newborn time: she was isolated, lacking roots and the support of a community. "I'm friendly, honest and very open with people," she says, "but over the years I've acquired very few friendships, without knowing why. I lived in ten different places before age eighteen, going to three different high schools."

At twenty-seven, she seemed ingenuous, unprepared for possible problems after childbirth. Although she had been hospitalized years earlier for treatment of psychotic states, she had gained little insight into the experience.

"The hospitalizations starting in 1979 never had any clear-cut diagnosis attached to them," Betsy says:

> I was twenty years old, living with my boyfriend, doing drugs and alcohol. My parents had just moved out of the country to Greece; I didn't know what I wanted to do. I was trying to "find myself" and I "found myself" in the Greater Milwaukee Mental Health Complex. I still don't know why or how I got there, even to this day, and I really don't know if it may have anything to do with the postpartum psychosis. I was hospitalized for three and a half months.
>
> The only things I can remember about those earlier states are bits and pieces. I thought I was Jesus Christ. Being relatively shy most of my life did not explain the fact that I remember standing up on tables, shouting to the other patients words I do not recall.
>
> The following year I was hospitalized in Greece for six months, where I not only was on medication but had a series of six "shock treatments." I came back to the U.S. that year and lived with my grandparents until the following year when I was admitted to a state hospital for four months. I remained in an outpatient program and finally at twenty-two years old got back on my feet enough to move into my very own apartment. Shortly thereafter, I got my own job as a medical transcriptionist. I threw away all my prescription drugs—I had side effects, but my determination was more powerful than they were. I licked drugs completely and did it on my own, very thankful I didn't get "hooked" on cocaine or anything else.
>
> In 1983 I met my beloved husband, and we have been very happily married for the past three and a half years.
>
> I never felt better in my entire life than during my pregnancy. I had no morning sickness and was famished for the majority of the time, gaining a total of eighty pounds.
>
> I went into labor at midnight and had contractions every five minutes until six A.M. when I called my obstetrician. He told me to meet him at the hospital. He was due to go on vacation the very next day. He artificially ruptured my membranes which of course means that they will not allow you to go home because of the "risk of infection." My doctor then let me walk around for a grand total of half an hour to "get my labor pattern started." At the end of half an hour my doctor said to me, "Okay, Betsy, let's get that smile off your face."
>
> A pitocin induction was started which now I am sure was only because the doctor didn't want to be with a laboring patient the day that he was due to be on vacation. It felt like a train was ripping through my body with every contraction, which occurred every two or three minutes for the next ten hours. I thought I was going to

die, that it would never end.

David was born at 8:45 P.M. I was so thrilled, so happy after my husband yelled, "It's a boy!" The first night in the hospital I was up till one A.M. talking on the phone, telling everyone about our newborn. I felt such great love and joy and thanks to God for having given us such a beautiful baby boy!

I started breastfeeding David immediately after delivery. We were in the hospital for five days together. I would estimate that I got, at best, fifteen hours of sleep while in the hospital. I was ecstatic with our son! I felt as though I was the only woman who had ever given birth in this whole wide world. I was so happy, I just couldn't wait to go home and play "Happy Homemaker and Mommy."

My husband John, David and I spent the first twenty-four hours at home together just by ourselves, and things couldn't have been better, or so I thought. My mother and sister drove down from New Hampshire and just my mom was going to spend the next week with us. My sister went back home the next day.

I didn't eat, I didn't sleep. My mind was racing from one thought to another so fast that the pen in my hand couldn't keep up with everything that I just "had to write down." I had grandiose ideas as to all the wonderful things I was going to do. I had nowhere near enough time to do all the things on my lists.

I remember breastfeeding David one midnight. He had finished eating and was lying in my arms, sleeping quietly. I didn't want to put him in his bassinet to sleep. I remember wanting him to lie there peacefully, just as he was, forever. I finally did put him to bed at about three in the morning, but then I would lie in bed for hours with a little flashlight next to me, planning out "everything I was going to accomplish for the next day."

My mother called the Obstetrics Floor of the hospital I delivered in to ask them for suggestions as to what to do for me. Their suggestions resulted in my taking long luxurious bubble baths while drinking wine or champagne, none of which really worked to get me to slow down or relax.

My speech was so rapid, but my thoughts were racing so fast that my mouth couldn't keep up with them. This went on for about two days. Finally the thought of taking me to the hospital was brought up. This was after my being up all night with scarcely one hour of sleep, and I was up and raring to go at four A.M. The night before, I had only about two hours of sleep.

Initially, we thought I might just be able to go to the Emergency Room and get a shot to calm me down and maybe they would send me home to rest. As we found out, this was far from the truth. On my tenth postpartum day my husband and grandmother took me to the Emergency Room. It took three hours of pacing and feeling as though I were going to jump out of my skin before I finally got admitted. I talked with one of the staff for a while, said good-bye to my husband and grandmother, was given a handful of pills and sent to bed, having been put on constant observation. It seemed like the longest time before I finally fell asleep that night.

It was hell being on that psych unit, but after having been there for only a few weeks, the worst part of it was that I was becoming quite dependent on it. I could do what I wanted for the most part, got my meals brought to me and didn't have to face any type of responsibility. They had me so drugged that I couldn't walk right, I didn't want to do anything.

I remember only glimpses of what happened during the first few weeks. I remember having a staff member with me at all times, even in the shower. I wasn't able to have a normal thought pattern such as getting dressed and THEN doing tasks. I would put on my underwear and maybe a sock and then try to get everything done within an hour that would normally take me the whole day. The staff told me that the Unit's kitchen was spotless as I apparently kept it clean. I remember tearing out many different types of pictures from magazines. I had all sorts of ideas about making collages and organizing coupons.

I got off constant observation after two weeks. I was given some "home passes" to go home and see how things went, but they were usually only for a few hours and I always had to be back at the hospital by that night. My diagnosis was "manic-depressive illness," the newest description of which is "bipolar disorder," even though I had no depression whatsoever. I agreed to take lithium after about five weeks in the hospital.

This manic episode that I experienced with David's birth was never attributed to the birthing process or the postpartum period. They just seem to slap on a diagnosis that seems to suit you, label you and treat you as such. I've been very bitter about that.

There were quite a few complications of my hospital stay. One of these was the fact that my psychiatrist went on vacation during the last two weeks I was in the hospital. By that time I was a complete and utter zombie. Another psychiatrist stepped in, this time a woman. She seemed to do much more for me, since I was discharged two weeks later. For instance, the previous psychiatrist had me on some kind of drug which made it so I could not feel my feet, wash my hair, take a worthwhile shower or brush my teeth; the day before I was taken off this medication, I was not able to get out of the car without help.

Since I was on the Psych Unit for seven weeks total, I had to have my "six-week postpartum checkup" while in the hospital. I was "with it" enough to ask my obstetrician about this "postpartum psychosis," why was nothing mentioned to me about the fact that this might happen, what were my chances of this happening to me again, what can I do to prevent this from happening again, why, why, why? The only response that I got from him was, "I don't know. That's not my forte. You'll have to discuss it with your psychiatrist." By this time I was fuming inside. He just literally washed his hands of me and my postpartum experience completely.

I was discharged from the hospital on lithium and Cogentin. Every time I went to the Outpatient Clinic and asked my doctor how I could get off the lithium, I always got the same answer: "I'm here to help you. If you don't want the help, you don't belong here." I decided long before I was discharged that I was not going to be on lithium for the rest of my life and was going to be off it as soon as possible. We found a psychiatrist who supported me and my ideas, said that it's my body and I know more about it than anybody else, agreed with me that my condition was attributable to childbirth and the tremendous changes a woman's body undergoes afterwards, and said basically that I was going to try to go off the lithium anyway and who was he to stop me? I gradually reduced the dosage over the course of a year, and have been off lithium for three months now, and feel great. My only hope is that I will never need it again.

Since her recovery, Betsy has had an increased problem with premenstrual mood swings. She has begun to look for insight into her vulnerability, as well as new ways of handling it:

I've been made aware of ACOA (Adult Children of Alcoholics), thinking I may have something there. My way of reasoning is that since my mother, father, his parents and my mother's parents have all either been alcoholics or are dead due to some effects of alcohol, that somewhere along the line I may have lost some genetic blocks that people are usually born with. I've also wondered about such things as whether certain alcoholic characteristics such as perfectionism would have something to do with the way I fly off the handle at every "little" thing that doesn't go the way I want it to.

I'm still battling with PMS tremendously. When I hear that it only gets worse as time goes on, I get to feeling totally helpless and hopeless as to which way to turn with this syndrome. I'm trying to treat it as a stress in my life by riding my bike and walking. John and I also are starting to try to give me one whole hour during the day to call mine to do whatever I want as a break away from routine, whether it's to go soak in the tub or go to the library, to paint my fingernails or just walk by myself. I've given up caffeine totally except giving up the chocolate is pure torture for me!

Betsy reflects on the possible cause of her manic episode after David's birth, and its effect on her relationship with him:

> I think the cause of my experience was childbirth itself, perhaps a hormonal imbalance of some kind. Lithium, they say, replaces a salt that your body lacks. Perhaps it was a salt that my body was missing. I also think my tremendous weight gain during my pregnancy had something to do with it. The fact that the doctors and nurses in the hospital after the delivery did not spot anything wrong with me was also a factor.
>
> I loved David so much. Nothing could have interfered with the love I felt towards him, until I had to be admitted to the hospital a second time, without my baby. Then my feelings changed to guilt: "What did I do wrong?" I no longer loved David the way I had in the beginning. I also had to stop breastfeeding just as soon as they gave me that handful of pills. That was very traumatic for me because I wanted to be successful in that aspect of mothering.
>
> I talked with John about my feelings but they were so hard to express, especially when my husband wasn't really even being allowed to bond with David himself, with everybody else around him, especially the women, thinking they could change a diaper, burp the baby, feed the baby, so much better than John could. I'm happy we struggled through this experience together as I know it has made our relationship that much stronger. I knew my feelings toward David would eventually change, and they definitely have. I love him just as much as ever now.
>
> When I was in the hospital without David, my grandmother and John brought him in to see me as often as I found I could "handle" it. Most of the time I was too weak to hold him and I remember being so afraid I would never be able to pick him up or hold him ever again but I can do it now!
>
> I am very thankful that my family was there with me after coming home from the hospital the first time with David, for they were the only ones who were able to say, "Gee, this really isn't our Betsy. Something's wrong."

But Betsy also feels that the presence of extra people was too stressful. "If I have to do again," she says, "I would not let ANY family near my husband, son and myself until at least a week or two had gone by."

> I'm also thankful that as far "out of it" as I really was, I was still able to know and say that maybe I'd better go back to the hospital. I can

135

only say now that with the help and strength of God and my husband and family, I am very much better, healthier and wiser today for having gone through such an experience.

I hope that I have learned to speak up for my rights and my own decisions, especially in regards to my health, be it physical or mental. I would like to think that I am able to forgive and forget, live and let live. Perhaps if I could not do these things before the experience, I can do them better now.

I so much want to have my next pregnancy go smoother. I pray that I will have my second postpartum period go similar to your second postpartum period. That is, being careful to sleep, being determined to stay "grounded," and yes, I even pray that I will feel a bit depressed for a couple of days!

~   ~   ~

Alicia: Allies In Wonderland

"I am a woman on a path," says Alicia Russell-Smith. "Open to the universe, learning to get my feet wet, hands dirty in the day to day reality of this life on this plane. I am creative, full of ideas I work to translate in my writing and the quilts I design and execute ... I am a mother, taking that road seriously. I am a visionary."

For Alicia, moments of altered awareness began occurring long before the birth of her child, and escalated afterwards into a lengthy period of "transformed perception." Many of Alicia's vision/hallucinations included her newborn son. Though they were sometimes frightening, she believes they helped her maintain a bond with her baby during the separation caused by his premature birth. Six weeks after Anthony's birth, Alicia wrote:

> For me, the altered awareness started in pregnancy. During and after childbirth, things got more intense. A lot of color transference and overlays of colors on "ordinary" objects—I have been very aware of colored auras surrounding people. Some auditory hallucinations and a sense of strong communication links with my son via sounds which are not "really there," and very intense 3-D visions which I believe he feels as well.

It seemed as though the border between dream world and outer world was opened, allowing fantasy images to impinge upon her senses. "I've attributed much of this to sleep deprivation and a relaxed mental gate keeper," she wrote, "so I am no longer distinguishing `reality' as something linear."

Perhaps she was also seeing and hearing into subtle dimensions of the world, as she reached out mentally for contact with her baby:

The strongest and most vivid alterations were from the pushing stage of delivery through the week following birth, when Anthony and I were separated—him in an I.C.U. and me at home. I feel the experiences of transformed perception were a way of staying close to him and maintaining our bonding link.

At the time, they scared, overwhelmed and exhilarated me. I felt special as if I ought to cherish the impressions and myself. As if I must somehow integrate and learn from them. Now, six weeks later, the "flashbacks" are still happening. I find that they occasionally make me nervous (are they here to stay) and fearful (how will I keep them to myself or avoid sounding crazy?). Fortunately I've only been expected to care for Anthony and can thus roll with the cosmic punches a lot more than I could if I had to maintain a "front" outside my own chosen, safe environment.

There are two prevalent themes for the visions, which usually lead me to a sense of being in the visions, not my living room, hospital, post office etc., the actual places I find myself when they occur. The themes: high speed animations where everything is a cartoon and Anthony and I are watching the "films" together and commenting on what we see. Another more intense sensation is that we are animals: most frequently bears, dolphins and wildcats. Sharp sensations of animals' physical environments, the smells and sounds. This occurs most frequently during nursing.

A lot of Alice in Wonderland type stuff: quite tall, feet too large. Very small and scurrying. A few times, I've awakened with a sense of crossing currents; I am in other bodies, rooms etc., before I really focus on my true physical location. Many transference experiences in the garden—I become various plants, particularly flowers. I have greeted many herb devas and have been a pea sprout pushing itself through the ground. I look at people and know a little more than they say. In empty rooms I get sensations of things which may have happened there. I have strong senses of déjà vû which don't just stop at having been here before—I go on realizing entire lives and universes which lead up to the point of recollection.

With her baby two months old, Alicia wrote, "I have finally stopped feeling like I am on an incredible journey twenty-four hours a day. My body is definitely `itself' again and my mind and thought patterns are integrating pre-Anthony tape loops. Having a little perspective is quite useful in such an overwhelming experience, I'm finding. I thought, since you seemed interested, that I'd go into a little more depth about my experience."

Here is Alicia's story as it unfolded in letters written during the first year after Anthony's birth:

I'll start at the beginning which was, for me, conception. I had been pretty hooked into my biological imperative for several months prior to our active attempts to have a baby and we succeeded almost immediately. When we did, I knew because I got very trippy and blissed out during a stressful time, and I started floating—this lasted a week and then I got freaked out. What if I wasn't pregnant? What if I miscarried (I'd had two abortions and was concerned with the karmic wheel of justice)?

In the middle of my panic, there was a stillness which started in my belly and spread through my body. When I slowed my brain enough to hook into the sensation, I felt a firm grip at the side of my uterus. I could "see" the little embryo (radiating magenta and electric blue) clinging to me.

Weeks progressed and I started feeling the physical sensations I knew to mean pregnancy (most noticeably, morning/everytime sickness). I got an early home testing kit and realized I had another week to wait for accuracy. In that week, I was incredibly uptight. One night I sat at my desk and summoned every shred of meditative awareness I had, turning my mind deep inward to blackness and the throb of untapped power. Okay, I said. I need to know right now. Am I or aren't I.

After a few seconds of swirling darkness, I was standing in a mist which shifted black-grey-steel blue, then vibrant blue. Then a blue and magenta dove swooped down and I caught its tail feathers. Our course made a loopy trail of pink and magenta in the "sky." The dove led me to my uterus, in which resided a tiny little fetus, its heart beating wildly. The fetus was brilliant blue; the dove scratched the male sign in the sky—it glowed silver and stayed in my brain after the experience ended. Two days later I had a positive test.

A few weeks later I was in our garden. The grass was very high, the beds unweeded. (Unkempt, untampered-with plants and vegetation, particularly in bloom, are pretty traditional sites of deva activity.) I had planted a lot of borage, to attract bees. Then, I read that the leaves were a good source of calcium for pregnant and lactating women. I plucked a few and ate them, then ate a few of the flowers.

Almost at once, the yard swam in violet, blue and silver. The dew on my feet felt heavy and very noticeable; I was super-aware of each drop and the way rivulets ran from my ankles down my foot, between my toes. There was an incredible, melodic hum in the air. Bees (my first true love) were everywhere and then I started to see "them"—the little borage devas. Long curly hair and silverly violet togas. They sang to me and brushed against me, urging me to be strong and healthy. A group of them circled the ground and I squatted down to find, nestled in the grass, the little fetus-vision.

I had the impression I could have touched it, but I got almightily scared and sort of fainted or blacked out. Came to almost at once and the back yard was normal. Went in the house feeling shaken. Jim (whom I did not tell until much later) found four or five bees in my hair. The grass got cut and this stopped before anything else happened, which I'm both sad and glad about. It really scared but fascinated me at the same time.

Right around then I started thinking of and calling the baby Anthony though everyone else hoped or expected I'd have a girl. We had great in utero communication—I told him how much I loved him and wanted him to be healthy. We developed a morning ritual—he'd be up, kicking all night until six or seven A.M., then we'd both crash out till ten or eleven, then I'd wake up and he'd be still. I'd say okay, pal, show me you're there, and he'd kick and roll over, then we'd doze for another hour. I always felt very connected to Anthony during the pregnancy, and had persistent visions of birthing him and then licking him clean—not one of the animal fantasies but me, as myself, birthing and licking him. In fact when he was born, I wanted badly to do this but was afraid of others' reaction if I did.

When I went into labor prematurely, I stopped feeling connected—I was scared of the pain and also unsettled by everyone preparing me for a possible C-section and postpartum separation. Labor was straightforward—the midwives called it a "good" labor but it was weeks before I grasped their meaning. It hurt, a fact I repressed as long as possible. I had to wear the fetal monitor continually and this really screwed me up, plus the fact that I was holding back a little—fear of worse pain—fear the baby would be grotesque and I couldn't handle it.

Finally, Valerie, the midwife, took off the monitor and put Jim and me in the bathroom. I had an incredible contraction and looked into Jim's eyes to breathe with him—the only time I used this practiced technique. I felt myself opening and as I stared at Jim, his pupils dilated in the exact rhythm of my cervix's dilation (I went from 3.5 to 9.5 centimeters on that contraction). When his pupils got to the edge of his irises I freaked out, thinking we'd both explode. That's when the cartoons started—I "saw" the explosion—like the roadrunner blowing up the coyote—and from then on labor was a cartoon—I still think of it as such, with the Loony Tunes theme music.

At last Anthony crowned and then spurted out before anyone could catch him. When I felt his arms and legs hitting the backs of my legs, I transcended time and space and just went nuts with ecstasy. They told me it was a boy and I started yelling I KNEW IT! Anthony was small-but-big-for-a-preemie. Instantaneous bonding between him and me—we already *knew* each other.

While nurses, midwives, etc. were in the room, he was very cagey—he came out with an intense frown and would only open one eye to peer with obvious suspicion. When I was cleaned up, etc. they told me we could only have an hour or so because his breathing was "wrong." I'd seen Valerie try to get the other midwife's eye without alerting Jim or me—I knew something wasn't right but I couldn't register pain or anxiety yet—just euphoria. *What* a high.

As soon as everyone left, Jim dimmed the lights. Anthony opened his eyes and looked back and forth between us with an expression of great calm and wisdom. It was incredible to add emotional depth and understanding to the "bonding" I'd read so much about.

Then he was gone (Jim went to the nursery with him). I lay in the bed thinking this was my last shot at solitude for awhile. That's when the animal things started. I replayed the bonding, only this time I unwrapped Anthony (they bundle preemies) and licked him clean—suddenly I was a bear in a cave—could smell the damp earth floor of it, could feel rocks against my back. Was licking Anthony and he suckled at me (in "real life," this disinterested him when they tried to attach him to my nipple). There was a stream running through the cave. I "stayed a bear" until Jim returned with Anthony's statistics and Apgar scores.

You wrote of things being little and babylike and that reminded me of the Brussels sprout incident. The night after I came home from the hospital, without Anthony (he went to another hospital's infant I.C.U.), my mom came to stay and care for us. She made dinner and Jim brought it to me on a tray. There was a dish of Brussels sprouts which I stared at—they looked like babies' heads. They all turned and looked up at me. When I ate one, I heard Anthony crying (both Jim and I experienced this many times during our separation from our son).

When we chose things for Anthony's homecoming they would vibrate blue, pink, lavender, magenta. Anthony's image would be superimposed on the objects (blankets, undershirts, a teddy bear). I found myself going into stores and walking right to the things Anthony needed, the exact objects he was "supposed" to have. I had a lot of times when things got silvery and then went to "reverse negative," with Anthony superimposed on the "real" image.

When I would actually see Anthony during a hospital visit, he would levitate and float, we'd both seem to be dolphins, bears or foxes. The levitations were kind of hallucinatory energy imprints, like an out of focus hologram of Anthony zooming around in the air. I now realize in real stress the cartoons started. Mellower times I perceived us as animals. One week after his birth, I wrote:

> *I wear black because if not,*
> *the colors reflect too sharply and get "confused"*
> *in space somehow. I hear their little*
> *popgun wars all around me. How can*
> *I control the urge to lick Anthony's*
> *milky face clean? We have fur. Grey and*
> *sometimes mottled brown. I can*
> *smell it, slightly damp. Meanwhile the*
> *colors are sharp and vivid. This is love.*

In between altered states, I was frantic for my baby. I spent long, hard days sitting with him on an uncomfortable chair while my stitches throbbed. We developed a real rapport then. I would stare at him and talk to him in a language which sounded like gibberish but meant things (I don't know what, now that I'm "normal").

Once home, the lightning bolts of bright white energy started. I got scared—Jim and I had both noticed an undercurrent of spirits in the house for the two years we've been here. Meditated and Anthony "told" me—I am helping you grow strong. One night I awoke to find myself having an intense out of body experience—hand to hand combat (like the end of the second Star Wars flick) with a former lover. The energy level was incredible and I was as scared as I've ever been. I reached out for Jim and realized Anthony was awake (he sleeps between us) and staring at me calmly, with a look of incredible wisdom and understanding. The room was full of hot-white lightning bolts. I realized a great psychic battle had been fought and I'd apparently won. Since then, the energy level has indeed been sweet and benign—the fulfillment of Anthony's in utero promise.

August—Anthony five months old

I am back to "my old self" and yet, it's all different now, because of Anthony. What a beast now that he's aware of the outside world! He's a happy little boy, very bright and curious and I feel (and know I am) fortunate. I still get occasional very intense and painful anxiety attacks when I remember the Early Days but I just keep telling myself: we both survived the separation. I am past the guilt (I think!) of interrupted bonding. I feel so close to my child and we have such a nice rapport going that I don't think I need to get too hung up on it.

I have been having some pretty intense spiritual stuff go on, all of which I can trace back to the birth and subsequent hallucinations. Based on pure subjective experience, post birth altered consciousness is fascinating and deep reaching.

An event which fractured my confidence for over a week: I was trying (valiantly) to finish a writing project—I looked at my hands on the typewriter keys and they melted. It was a long time before I "risked" looking in a mirror, I can tell you! That experience taught me something about self image and inner power. I have been stumbling towards a vision quest, I think, and am going from interest to obsession with Native American spiritualism. I believe the birth opened my willingness to suspend any need-for-credibility and just follow my instincts.

The continuing thing is these weird dreams (the kind you later wonder: was I awake or did I dream that) which vary in content. The main thing is that I have an "energy force confrontation"—and the force comes at me and invades my body. I "wake up" thinking I'm about to explode—really unsettling but later I try to figure out what it meant.

I started having these dreams in this house and they've always been here except one in my mom's place in Maine. So that means two and a half years, but since Anthony's birth (I didn't have them while pregnant; I believe he protected me from them/myself) they have been in color and really sensaround, 3-D affairs and I believe they are not necessarily bad. I used to be terrified of them. I sometimes "come to" and open my eyes during the sequence and have seen the air shimmering with golden light . . .

October—seven months

For awhile, Anthony was nursing almost exclusively and the animal hallucinations came back—they were really nice, idyllic images of us as whales swimming in a peaceful sea. So I'm beginning, in my own mind, to make some connection between nursing hormones and the "phenomenon." Another factor to consider— sleeping arrangements. We have a family bed and I believe this too contributes to the hallucinatory tie to Anthony.

I had my first postpartum period three weeks ago and now I feel like I have PMS—for a long time I didn't "believe" in it and saw it as another ripoff, marketing strategy to hit women where they are most vulnerable. Now, I'm less sure. I feel like a collection of jagged edges.

I am still settling in to, not only motherhood, but also in-the-house syndrome. Winter is coming FAST. It has been a little difficult to find myself "stuck in the house." Jim is supportive and a very active parent but I still encounter money problems and image problems. When I worked I more or less had whatever I wanted, though I rarely saw it that way—now I have to rely on the kindness of others for some "spare change."

The sensaround dreams I described to you have hit a disturbing peak where I feel I was warned to either commit myself (to whom or what I don't know) or back off. I took a day on a mountainside (alone—what a luxury and one I will never take for granted again!) to ponder my goals and need to seek—power and awareness—to attempt to visualize a balance between this and the demands and commitment of motherhood.

One of my problems with my own mother and our relationship was that she was never "there"—didn't really nurture me full time and only paid close attention when I was particularly clever and interesting. This isn't my intent or desire with Anthony, so it means a pretty full time focus. Which means I can't be trekking off into the woods every whipstitch for "retreats."

I felt pregnancy and birth awakened so much awareness and raw potential as a conductor of power and now I am frustrated by not knowing how to use it, or feeling I don't have the energy to explore what could be.

Looking back two years after her son's birth, Alicia wrote, "I was capable of a great 'absorption' the first year of Anthony's life because I was so spiritually tossed-about and susceptible. I believe birth is indeed a vision quest and through its passage we move deeper into our secret lives. We tap their energy almost subconsciously; we lead ourselves into the possibilities without even seeing what we're doing. And ultimately, we make room for the voices and images which are not flesh and blood or mortar and steel (or microchips). I think this is ecstasy . . . without the aches and pains of out-and-out insanity."

11

Through Anger And Loss

*A*s with any great change in life, the birth of a child presents us with both gain and loss. Thus our reactions to it are seldom simple, but complex and ambivalent. For some parents, experiences during childbirth itself are a source of prolonged feelings of betrayal and anger. For a few, there is the emotional pain caused by serious problems or even death of their child. But for all parents, an element of loss is a natural part of their experience in the newborn year.

No matter how welcome and wanted, a baby's arrival means some loss of the person that one used to be. Some forms of personal freedom are greatly curtailed, especially for the new mother. Old activities, even ones that once were part of her identity, fall to the wayside. She may not realize how much her sense of worth was bound up in them, until they're gone. How many parts of her life can she give up and still feel she is herself?

> Motherhood has taken a big bite out of my creative pursuits, which used to define my sense of self. Now being a wife and mother is demanding my attention, a role that I sometimes resent. I am, however, learning that creativity exists in everything I do, including mothering, and that is where I'm needed. I'll be able to write poetry again someday, if the urge hasn't left me.
>
> - Karen Bard

> Since I had my son, I haven't been gainfully employed, and although I seriously think it's good for the children, it's been pretty damaging to my psyche.
>
> - Susie Helme

Relationships change and some may be lost. "There is a divide you scarcely know about until you're on the other side," says one mother, "and suddenly you're one of the parents, not one of the children." Some marriages don't survive the demand that both partners grow up. Some friendships don't survive the transition of one person to parenthood with its new focus. A woman writes:

I had a lonely feeling that I was divided now from everyone who was not a parent—and even from my former self. I knew that the change I felt in myself was not something I would be able to communicate to anyone who hadn't experienced it. Sad but true, over the years since my first child was born, I've grown distant from old friends who aren't parents themselves.

It's possible to feel persecuted by the baby who now demands so much time and attention. As he grows into a toddler, there is the exhausting boredom that can overtake a mother when his daylong activities frustrate her own emerging interests.

From the beginning, babies are individuals who differ in their demands upon us. It can be a shock to discover that this tiny person can push us to the limit of our self-control. When the pressure is too great, the support too slim and our isolation unendurable, dangerous levels of anger build up. It may be hard to recognize and admit the intensity of these feelings.

"I actually didn't realize I was such a mess until my daughter was about eighteen months old," says Sally Stevens. "She was a fussy demanding baby, had to be carried all the time and didn't like her brother Billy having any part of his Mommy." Sally's unrecognized pain arose, she says, "from anger, but more generally being overwhelmed by my two children, my sense of perfectionism, isolation. I grew up in a home that didn't include much affection or warmth, and that was definitely carried over in the boarding school where I had lived."

Ironically, Sally was a counselor for other mothers through La Leche League, yet didn't realize her own need for more support. She recalls:

> My husband was leaving for work at 6:30 A.M. and not getting home until 6:30 P.M. or later. I had no time for Billy and found myself yelling at him all the time. I did almost no housework and spent a lot of time out of the house driving—making up errands just to be away from the house. My husband and I had sex maybe once every four to six weeks. I was not aware of touch and perceived it from a long way off even though I was nursing. Everything else felt far off, too.
>
> I hated being a mother but went from one day to the next just to get through them. I kept going and leading La Leche League meetings telling the mothers who came for help that their lives would improve as their babies got bigger, or solving other people's problems when they called on the phone for help.
>
> I honestly don't remember a lot about the day to day experience except that I'd rather not go through anything like it again. It was a dark part of my life and I can't blame or put my finger on any one thing that caused it. I felt overwhelmed, out of control and angry. I'm afraid to get pregnant again.

Sally's emotional pain eased when she finally was able to recognize it:

> Some time during Ellen's eighteenth month I just realized how out
> of control I was. I felt like I'd reached the end of a long tunnel. I
> seem now to be more aware of myself—my moods. I try to spend
> extra time with Billy. I try to talk more about how I'm feeling to
> Richard and the children. I started a support group for mothers
> with small children. We need help; we need each other to get
> through the tough days.

Sally suggests, "Get support from people you know and trust before you
have the child—make sure you are aware that everything may not be roses and
ribbons after the baby is born."

~   ~   ~

Many parents are still hurting from the way they were treated during the
time of their children's birth. In stories recalling delivery, the levels of anger
are often staggering. And much of it is held inside; people often have difficulty
trusting their own reactions in the face of professional authority.

One of the hardships of hospital birth is to be surrounded by people who
don't know us and for whom our event is nothing special. Without meaning
to, they hurt our tender feelings and frustrate the need to honor ourselves and
the newborn.

A woman described how strange it was, as she left the hospital with her
baby, to catch a glimpse of the doctor who had attended the delivery—a man
she'd never met before. "To have shared such an intimate moment with a
stranger . . ." We sustain an emotional injury when these relationships are
ignored or immediately severed. Nancy Wendlandt, whose baby was delivered by caesarean, says:

> I felt a deep need just to *see* my surgeon sometime after the birth,
> but during my hospital stay, he never showed his face. Things felt
> incomplete. And still do.

Childbirth puts a woman in a double bind. It requires a willing surrender
to forces beyond her control, yet she needs to come through it with her self-
respect and dignity intact. She is physically so exposed and emotionally so
vulnerable that feelings of rage and humiliation are easily aroused.

Routine interventions, done with the intent to help, can leave parents
feeling powerless and cheated. A mother compares her no-intervention home
birth with an earlier delivery: "For the first time, I had no episiotomy. With my
daughter I was cut, so it seemed I went from hard pushing to plop out she fell.
I really felt in retrospect that her birthing was robbed from me."

Long after my daughter's birth, I hoped I was done with feeling hurt and hung up when I wrote:

> I was haunted for months by strange emotions about it—from the time I realized that the doctor had helped me push her out by using the vacuum forceps, without asking my permission or even telling me what he was doing, and why. I thought about her birth obsessively, remembering every little thing that could seem wrong and regretting the constant interruptions in our first day together.
>
> I was trying to discover the root cause of my anxiety about it— the real reason why I felt upset and uncomfortable each time I came up against the idea of "childbirth." That feeling that "something was done wrong" and "something was taken away from me" has never worn off entirely, though my womb no longer tightens in anger at the memory.
>
> It feels as though something interrupted the flow, got in my way; as though I almost got in touch with that tremendous energy, but was robbed of the chance by the doctor's decision. I have been furious with him for his interference with the timing of her birth, his cutting in on my first dance with that powerful energy.

It turns out that a woman's level of participation is the major factor in how she will feel about the delivery later. More important than the type of birth or the interventions that take place, is her sense of having authority, making choices and sharing in each decision. This can only happen with attendants who know and respect her as an individual.

The alternative, where she is "managed" and treated as a non-person, can leave her with feelings of violation and loss that she may not easily recognize. Mary describes her passage through such feelings:

> Water broke at three A.M., went to hospital; too tired to sleep. Started pitocin next afternoon. Hated the induced labor— screamed, cried, wanted to leave, wanted it over. Pushing was uncomfortable, too. Finally she was out and alert and perfect and looking like her dad.
>
> It took several years, lots of reading, lots of talking and working with pregnant people before I was able to admit how wrong my labor and delivery had been handled. (My doctor no longer induces under those circumstances.)
>
> Two years after her birth, I started my work as a pregnancy counselor. This is when the unacknowledged, unnoticed anger and grief came to my attention. When a nurse treated one of my clients with that "if you care about the baby, do as we say" attitude, I remembered. When a friend's bag of waters broke and my doctor never induced her—let her go four days—I remembered. When I

heard and read about all the things one can do to stimulate labor besides a pitocin drip, I remembered. When a doctor gave clients an epidural at nine centimeters, then pitocin because labor stopped, then an episiotomy because he had to shave before his office opened—I became enraged.

When my best friend's waters broke and she went straight to the hospital, had several vaginal exams, then a pit drip, then anesthesia for long hours—then gave birth to a baby with infection and respiratory distress—and believed she was GLAD she had the hospital there to help with this difficult birth, I just about went NUTS!

I did obsess for awhile then—I was SO uncomfortable in hospitals at that time! I even felt lucky to have had the labor I'd had—if I'd had an easy, no-intervention birth I would never have understood these situations, would never have done all the reading I did about preventing them, would never have realized how women feel they must regard the birth as wonderful when they are really hurt.

I couldn't go on like this forever of course. The book *Transformation Through Birth* by Claudia Panuthos really helped me get from the anger to the healing. But the most wild turning point was going to several lectures by Sheila Kitzinger. (She is superhuman!) When she talked about birth she was so realistic—when the conference was over I felt as if I'd HAD another child, an "ideal" birth—as if I had really experienced it. I noticed afterward that those little attachments to "doing it again and getting it right" were gone.

~ ~ ~

Parents suffer the deepest loss when their child is severely disabled or fails to survive. Our children make us so vulnerable, arousing such a strong need to protect them; to lose a baby at any time in the cycle of birth can be devastating. For some parents there is the additional pain of losing their faith in the God or nature that has allowed this to happen. Becky's baby died during premature delivery. She says:

> I believed in God and thought He was there to keep things like this from happening. I had confidence in religion but when this occurred we lost our feelings about the Church and that God really existed. We felt lost without any hope and nothing to fall back on.

Jann Light experienced what she called her "childbirth ecstasy" for several months after her son's birth (Chapter 9). Joyous insights and a clear sense of purpose illuminated her beliefs. But a few years later she was doubting those beliefs. Her story voices many feelings that accompany loss in the birth cycle: the pain that helps us empathize with others, and the anger that alienates us from uncaring nature and silent gods. She writes:

We stopped using birth control during the summer of 1983. The last week of October, 1985, I conceived. On October 31 there is a long entry in my journal about a baby I kept "seeing" in my mind and the dreams I had the night before about building the Statue of Liberty, meeting a child with Down's Syndrome in a parking lot and watching her ride away in a car, trying to explain to people why I was going to adopt a child with a disability.

These types of dreams—especially recurring were the ones about the child with accentuated physical characteristics of Down's Syndrome—continued for about three weeks. After my period was almost two weeks late I had a pregnancy test and it was positive. The odd thing was—I'll quote from my journal:

"The strangest thing is although I am convinced intellectually and I know there is an embryo growing inside I don't FEEL pregnant. I was excited the day I had the test done, but not overly so, and the next day I hardly thought about it. Now, a week later I still don't have that emotional "feeling pregnant" as if there were another spirit hanging around close by. Physically I feel sort of pregnant . . . But that intrinsic emotional knowledge and joy that were so ever-present and overwhelming during the other pregnancy are totally absent. In fact it was the first time in almost two years that I really felt absolutely sure I was not pregnant before my period."

I miscarried the next day. The next entry in the journal says something about being very upset and "unfortunately this is the strongest emotion I've felt in connection with the pregnancy. And still there's that distance, as if it's happening to someone else." (That day, by the way, was Thanksgiving.) For several days the detached feeling continued. I had felt during that time that the whole process was physical. I felt not so much that I had cut off any emotional reaction, but that something was wrong because I wasn't sad enough—there didn't seem to be any reactions to cut off.

But then as my body healed its hurt quickly, the emotions came with full force. I felt empty. I remember looking at the poplars that are all over Los Alamos and had just lost all their leaves and feeling just like them—empty. I did not want to be around happy people, celebrations, or distractions. I needed to be alone and sad.

After the first week of December there is about a six month break—not another entry until May. I remember those months as being time spent in deep introspection, playing lots of music, learning to draw and express myself that way and listening to everything by Gustav Mahler I could find. The experience of a death, which is what it was for me, so close (what could be closer than inside my body?) took me deep inside myself and far out into the world of humanity.

It was a chance to grow and face the interconnectedness of people—and especially parents—like no other experience I had had up to that point. At times I felt that I was mourning for all babies who had not had the chance to grow up. Other times it seemed more that I was mourning for any parent who had lost a child. The experience went from the intensely personal to almost cosmic proportions.

The mourning period lasted for a full nine months. The baby's due date was a day of sadness. We were trying in earnest to get pregnant then. "I woke with the thought of what today would have been. With the thermometer in my mouth already, I pushed the curtain aside to see—was it only early or was the sky as gray as my heart felt? No, it's not early, already after seven. It looks like one of those quiet days when it will snow three feet and leave people stranded and cold. But, although I am chilled now, I remember it is July.

Everything I do today: brush my hair, fix breakfast, the little kisses I receive from Adam, seems to have the after thought, `Today is the day I would be giving birth. Today is the day my baby would have been born.' We will go to the park and feed the ducks instead, Adam and I.

Life goes on as always, others do not remember and are not touched by her memory—no one else seems to remember what a grand day July 21 was to be—and the small lifeless embryo that escaped my loving willing womb. But today, today, the sky is my friend and is gray with sadness for her death." The pain lessens and other activities resume their place in life, but it is never forgotten and I have changed because of the experience.

In February of 1988 I got pregnant again. I did a home test on the morning of my birthday and got a positive result. What a wonderful birthday it was. I got the one thing I really wanted! Three weeks later I started bleeding and went into labor in the early morning hours of the ninth anniversary of the day I was married.

With the first miscarriage the pain had a tragedy and pathos to it which was almost beautiful in a way, maybe because I watched it with the eye of an observer. The second time there was not pathos or drama. It was an ugly hurt. The pain was violent and my emotional interaction with everything happening was that of anger. It was unfair, I was being cheated and if that Supreme Being (which was so perfectly clear in 1982) was still out there somewhere it had no relevance to my life.

In contrast to having an awakened awareness of "higher levels of life" in 1982, I am now questioning the existence and reality of those levels and of God. I wrote earlier about my awareness being expanded except that I was unaware of trouble, suffering, war, and so forth. During the week after this miscarriage I was burdened with those concerns. Drugs, gang wars, seven murders in Albuquerque in one weekend, people blowing up each other, the disappearance of the rain forest, the whales and the Mexican gray wolf, not to mention what is going on in Ethiopia . . . It was all too much for me. The most recurrent thought I had during that week was "Why do we bother?" ("We" being humans on the earth now.)

With close and caring friends, supportive family and counseling I am coming through it. But again I am changed. Mostly, I am angry. I'm angry that Thanksgiving can never fully be a day for me to be happy and thankful. Passover and my anniversary (first day of Passover was on our anniversary) will from now on have that much less joy. April Fools' Day will never again be funny, but always a cruel joke for me.

The euphoric, ecstatic, joyous and clarity-of-purpose experiences which prevailed in my life for the six months after Adam was born are very remote now, almost nostalgic. I yearn for them again; at times I would give anything to re-experience them or to lose the five years between then and now and just go back to that time of my life forever. Other times, usually in my more lucid moments, I do my best to put all my experiences into more rational perspective and spend my time enjoying being with my wondrous, healthy, intelligent, miraculous five-and-a-half-year-old Adam: Instead, we go to the park and feed the ducks . . .

Disillusionment is painful; anger can go on a long time. And yet, like the inevitable losses that come with parenthood itself, a loss of faith nudges us into a new level of maturity. In a letter two months later, Jann wrote:

The pain is not gone, the anger isn't gone, but I'm no longer overwhelmed by them, and even with all that may be going on, I'm somehow more at home than I used to be. I guess it's part of becoming adult and gaining a more accepting attitude.

12

Moving Toward Wholeness

*E*xperiences in the newborn year can be a catalyst of great change. Every part of our being is engaged in the birth and the new relationship with our baby, and this total involvement breaks down barriers within us. We become inwardly more open, more nearly whole, and this is a kind of healing.

Even the most painful and turbulent experience may lead toward healing. "Birth is a great cleansing," says Amy. "The physical toxins can affect us physically, but there are also emotional, psychical, spiritual changes taking place, toxins being released. Old stuff let go by the new life energy flowing through."

As in the old teaching story of cleaning the inkwell by pouring in fresh water, what comes up first may be very dark stuff indeed. Many factors contributed to the nightmare quality of newborn time for Amy. In a strange environment, a cold and rundown house, with no support people and a husband whose own anxiety and anger were causing him to "go out all the time," she struggled to care for a baby who woke up every two hours for the first three months. Amy describes the time after her first childbirth:

> Almost went out of my body, for a long time. Could have stepped over the threshold into death, but for this baby, attachment. Nothing on earth but this baby, pooping, peeing, crying, sucking. And pain, soreness (I tore two inches inside my vagina, had a nicked and swollen perineum). Felt always over-stimulated through my senses. Felt that I was perceiving the world as my baby did. So open, vulnerable, no armor. Almost being the child, as opposed to being the mother—an avoidance. I only realized this later—knew then only the openness of the new being.
>
> I didn't eat well enough while pregnant, so I was starving, nervous, anxious and in pain. I was going through great change: coming out of the clouds onto earth, the reality of motherhood, a baby, the relationship with my husband, the loss of my old self. It knocked the socks off my rosy idealizations of Madonna and child, brought out my repressed fears and anxieties, my anger towards my own mother.

And how does Amy evaluate this experience, in the context of her life which now includes a second child?

> The experience was initially negative, unpleasant, but brought about positive change and healing. Even my husband went through healing, especially with the second one. I've become grounded, cheerful, basically positive and happy. Old repressed anger and anxieties were cleansed through this birth experience. It was extremely valuable—earth-shaking. I needed to really come to terms with my self, find my core, my energy, my light.

Even without such radical catharsis, lives are changed. We move toward wholeness as we come to know parts of ourselves that have been unexpressed. "Before the birth of my first child," says Stacey Mott, "I was not a very `spiritual' person. I wasn't really in touch with that side of myself. Becoming a mother was a real catalyst for me. I felt more connected—to life, I guess—both to people in the world, and to the idea of a God, a spiritual force in the world."

Carolyn Kinch is another woman for whom the events of newborn time were the beginning of a spiritual life:

> The day of the birth, I felt what I later called a "presence" from the time I got up until I actually began labor—a rather defined sense that something very special was about to occur.
>
> The hours after birth were "mystical" to me. I felt like "Queen of the Universe"—beautiful, serene, and in total control . . . During the days that followed, I spent hours holding my son and connecting with feelings I had forgotten I ever had. All senses were heightened; it was a definite "natural high." I felt a compassion toward everyone . . . I was enormously sensitive. I felt instinctively attuned to my son's needs, and had a desire to protect him at all times.
>
> Before the birth, I was an "intellectual" with little tolerance for what I then perceived as "nonsense." My attitude has changed dramatically. I began a pursuit of self-discovery, a lifelong quest for spiritual understanding, exploring religious philosophies previously thought of as ridiculous.
>
> I think the birth process and its effect on life view will come to be seen as more and more important. Emphasis will return to helping the mother to get in touch with herself, helping her to trust her intuitive knowledge of what is right for herself and her baby.

While some people become newly aware of a spiritual dimension, others find they are "grounded" through the experiences of giving birth and parenting. Their lives become balanced through a more wholehearted involvement with the everyday world. Says Lynn:

I have been interested in altered states of consciousness without the use of drugs since a very early age. At age fourteen I had a mystical experience which altered my sense of myself and the universe. I began meditating at age seventeen and steeped myself in metaphysical literature.

Having a child totally changed my life, from self centered introversion to other centered and involved with the world. My son is my greatest teacher. Through him I have come to re-experience my own childhood and redirect the pathways of child rearing that I felt come up out of my past. This has brought freedom and compassion.

The most painful experiences can bring about the greatest changes as we seek to understand them. For Kendra, the slow process of healing from a traumatic birth experience led at last to "a very wonderful change" in her life:

I am thirty-eight, have a three-year-old daughter, and we now live with her father, although I single parented for two years. I have always been a thoughtful, caring, sensitive and intuitive person, and worked as a psychotherapist for six years. I then changed to bodywork, which I've done for six years. Three years ago I started taking classes in opening psychic abilities.

When my daughter was twenty-one months old I began channeling a spirit guide quite spontaneously. Although I had previously done some psychic opening, this was a quantum leap in my abilities. The guide first came through when I was in a very calm, loving space with a friend. My other psychic abilities also began to open dramatically at that time. I am now a professional channel. I believe that this opening was prompted by the great deal of personal awareness work I did following my daughter's birth.

During labor I became quite psychic and able to tell how other people were feeling without even trying. This was by far the most psychic I had ever been to that time. Toxemia was diagnosed during labor. When I was about nine centimeters dilated I felt very stuck and unable to progress. I knew that my daughter's father was holding her back psychically because he was really afraid of becoming a father. Finally, I asked him to leave the room, and almost immediately went into pushing. The birth happened soon afterwards.

When my daughter was born, she needed intensive suctioning. She was brought to me for a few minutes when she was about ten minutes old, but I don't remember that. After I was taken to the ward alone—she was in Intensive Care—I just felt numb and helpless. I had been shocked to find she couldn't be with me. When I finally saw her at nine hours I burst into tears and felt some degree

155

of inner peace as I held her. I didn't see her again until she was twenty-two hours old, and somewhere in there something inside me gave up and I lost whatever a mother needs to bond with her newborn baby.

Even though I was an incredibly conscientious mother I felt very emotionally estranged from my baby, and the lack of ability to form a bond at birth was not healed until she was about eighteen months old. At that age I finally was able to feel that I loved her.

Like so many women who have distressing experiences around childbirth, Kendra lacked the necessary support: "I had very little support emotionally. My partner was in a state of shock and unavailable emotionally. My roommates did the minimum of physical care for me, for which I was really grateful." She continues:

The birth experience was tremendously traumatic for me, and in the months that followed I really worked on trying to understand how and why I had created such a situation in my life, and what I needed to learn. In the process I stripped away enough of my personality that I became clear enough to allow a connection with another spiritual being. It is not possible to channel or be psychic if there is too much "noise" from the personality. The ability to create a still inner space (as one does when meditating) is essential.

I am sure I would have opened to channel eventually, but that the resolution of the birth trauma speeded the process a great deal. After my spontaneous opening I took classes in channeling, and am now assisting others to open in this way, and doing readings professionally. I have experienced highly accelerated personal and spiritual growth and now feel a much greater sense of life purpose, inner power and self-sufficiency than ever before. It has been a very wonderful change in my life. Channeling has helped me tremendously to understand my life experiences and life path, and to understand my daughter's karma and personality. This has really helped what has not been an easy relationship.

Anne Calajoe experienced "a definite breakthrough" in the months after her first child's birth. "The birth had such an impact on so many levels. I think I had a great fear of childbirth and when I worked that fear through it released me. I didn't realize how strong and deep the fear was until I felt this profound release after my son's birth." She says:

The labor was long, hard and more painful than I could ever have imagined. I was amazed myself at how much endurance I had. After thirty-six hours of continuous back labor, I had an emergency C-section.

The time between when my doctor told me I would need a C-section and when I was put under anesthesia seemed like an eternity. They told me I couldn't push anymore—it was agony and the contractions came one after the other. I remember being in such pain and having to lie still and I kept saying in my mind, all I have to do is breathe and concentrate and when I awaken I will see my baby. I felt detached, lonely, isolated and disappointed and just wanted to enter a painless state at this point.

Despite the pain of her labor, Anne says, "It was worth every contraction. I was amazed and in awe at the baby's perfection the minute I saw him and held him in my arms. It was like a magnetic force surrounding us. I also was shaking uncontrollably and completely exhausted." Anne continues:

It took me a few days to admit I was disappointed and sad. I felt that the difficulty of the labor was like a failure on my part; at the same time I realized I did everything possible to try for a natural birth. I felt cheated of the birth experience and sad because I wasn't there to greet my little one into the world.

I was having difficulty sorting the whole birth process out—I didn't know what hit me—I just knew it was affecting me physically, emotionally and spiritually. I couldn't understand why the birth had turned out this way after such a beautiful, uncomplicated pregnancy. Perhaps it was a control issue, but I was overwhelmed with my feelings. It took me about a month or six weeks to resolve, which I did by writing it out and talking to close supportive friends and my husband.

I've always viewed childbirth as the ultimate challenge for a woman, maybe because my mother instilled such fear in me regarding childbirth. I've had to work hard to confront this and other issues, but as a result I feel as though I have worked through many blocks within myself—physically, emotionally and spiritually. Even my breathing changed after the birth of my son—more expanded and deeper.

It became apparent to me about two months after his birth that there were definite changes occurring within me. From that point on, it has continued to deepen, expand and become clearer. By six months it was evident a breakthrough had occurred.

I came across a quote from *The Prophet* by Kahlil Gibran that I closely identified with: "Your pain is the breaking of the shell that encloses your understanding." This was so true for me, maybe because as a result of the pain and my awareness of my tolerance and endurance, I felt strong. The only way I can describe this was that I felt released—a new sort of inner freedom—something that has been unblocked and letting go. I felt I had transcended most of my fears, anxieties and insecurities, and was aware of unlimited potential.

At six months after birth, I remember a lot of anger came up. There were some conflicts with my mother-in-law over control issues regarding the baby. I got in touch with a lot of anger and rage in regard to how others try to control, defending myself and how I try to control others. I was able to feel an actual knot at my solar plexus and I decided I needed to do some work on the third chakra. Anger has always been a difficult emotion for me to express and my mother-in-law served as a catalyst in forcing me to confront it. I was even able to get in touch with anger at my own mother for instilling fears and controlling me and for not providing enough warmth and emotional nourishment to the feminine aspect of myself. I experienced an explosion, or upheaval, which facilitated the breakthrough and release.

It has sent me on a journey of contacting/exploring/confronting the feminine concept of the void/the dark space, even in a symbolic sense. I became aware of various blockages in my body that needed to be released, became aware of emotional conflicts and the internal negative mother complex and have confronted the many faces of the Animus. I gained awareness of the power center of the body in the third chakra, and the ability to confront and explore control issues in my life. Even questioning, if I needed to go through a C-section in order to examine the issue of control: was I able to surrender and let go when necessary?

Motherhood seemed to be my next step on the spiritual path. It put me in touch with lessons I needed to learn—the lessons of patience, humility, tolerance, giving selflessly to another, total service and unconditional love. I felt that I was surrendering my old self to a whole new aspect of self that had been blocked and buried within. Giving birth helped me discover a place within myself that was a very deep well of love and giving.

I felt that I had been searching to fill some unexplainable gap within myself—a void, perhaps. Suddenly, through motherhood, it feels complete—full-circle. A new child, still so in touch with the spiritual, heavenly realms, is so full of positive, open energy; being connected now in the physical sense makes me almost feel reborn myself.

Says Anne, "I've never had an experience as profound as this—that has changed how I think, act and live to this degree. I still feel this compelling, yet nourishing inquiry to go deeper and expand more fully. Because I've let go of old beliefs, attitudes and fears, I can live as the human being I really want to be. And I can allow myself to go through the gentle process of becoming."

~   ~   ~

For many women the birth of a child brings a step forward into maturity and new confidence. Rebekah Bridge recalls that after delivering her baby she felt "very loving, giving, grateful, blessed":

> I was pleased that my labor hadn't been painful, and that it was over. I was thrilled that the birth felt so good, so sensual. The baby was gorgeous. Her daddy was so helpful and supportive. The world was grand . . . I remember feeling better about myself than ever before.

This sense of affirmation may be rooted in the feeling that *I gave birth*, and yet it goes deeper. Giving birth is something we don't know "how to do" with the conscious mind. We have connected with a deeper source, something within ourselves or beyond our separateness: "I felt like I had tapped into the whole human racial stream—people have been doing this for eons and I felt a part of a great big whole." Sue Akerman recalls:

> The major experience for me during the birth, and after, was an overwhelming and clear sense that my baby was God and that I was God. My midwife later remarked that I seemed to possess unusual strength and that she "wasn't really needed," perhaps a contrast to my great dependency on her previously, during the pregnancy.

Such an experience is not tied to a "perfect birth." It can take many forms and come at any time. Sometimes the new confidence is in contrast to previous doubts. For Carolyn Kinch, the birth of her first child brought a sudden and lasting change:

> The labor was very short and the birth itself was handled rather crudely by the obstetrician I was seeing. When I asked if I could touch my son, he responded, "Sure, if you want to touch a cold, slimy thing." I felt a very strong and righteous anger toward this physician and toward my husband for not speaking up—we were essentially paying this man large amounts of money to mar what could have been a peak experience.
> Against hospital advice at the time, I nursed immediately and had rooming in, going home the day after delivery, again against staff advice. The hours after birth were "mystical" to me. I felt like "Queen of the Universe"—beautiful, serene, and in total control. I felt confident to handle any condition or situation which could threaten my son's welfare. Though I had felt fearful and inadequate

while pregnant, I felt completely competent from the moment of first breastfeeding.

Carol Miseo-Hardin is another woman for whom the experience of bonding with her newborn generated an entirely new confidence. She recalls:

> I perceived the world in two ways. One, I saw all the harshness I could imagine, and it was overwhelming. I wanted to protect Angela from "the world"—traffic, weather, noise, light, people. Not viewing them as I usually had in the past—but in relation to my daughter's freshness—her new ability to deal with all of it. The catch was that I was feeling as she was, as sensitive and aware as she.
>
> The second was much more uplifting. In seeing all that "craziness" I feared I could potentially fall apart or pass this vibe on to Angela and I didn't want to do that. But what did happen was great. I felt invincible. I felt all powerful. That nothing could happen to us that I could not deal with and handle properly. The sweetness of the experience I know emanated because of us as a unit. Not she or I by ourselves; but because we were united through love. What a new perception of bonding!

For some women, self-assurance develops gradually and only after many experiences that challenge it. Anne Carducci, a mother of five, describes how she was finally able to feel and express confidence in dealing with the birth of her last child:

> For the birth of my last baby I carefully selected a doctor who would give me the type of birth I wanted (I had wanted these things since our second was born in 1973!), and a family physician who insured my getting the type of care I wanted postpartum (a maximum twenty-four hour stay; the baby with me all the time from the moment of birth on). She was born very early on a Sunday morning following a completely unmedicated birth in the birthing room of our local hospital.
>
> I was very calm, very relaxed, very peaceful, as well as determined that no one on the staff would make me do something I didn't want to do. One nurse suggested I nurse only three minutes on each breast three hours apart; I told her that was incorrect information; that I'd done this four other times and if I needed any help I'd ask for it—she literally backed off away from my bed. It was almost as if I had given myself permission to fight for my baby and myself (something I'd had trouble doing before) since I had doctor support. I even got some sleep this time because I knew Maria was right there with me.

I went home within twelve hours after birth. My mind was very inwardly-turned to the baby and I was so calm! It was a very, very special time, and I'm still experiencing the "high" produced from giving birth the way I chose to—a lot of self-confidence and good feelings about myself.

~   ~   ~

In recent years there has been a tremendous surge of public awareness about the vulnerability of postpartum women. Books, articles and television programs have focused attention on the increased incidence of mental and emotional illness during the year after childbirth. This recognition is life-saving and long overdue.

However, we need to know that this stage of a woman's life can also bring creative and liberating changes. In the newborn year the possibilities of breakdown and breakthrough are closely related.

Feelings of confidence have power to pattern a new sense of self. Linette Jensen's remarkable story shows how this time, with its real dangers, also bears the potential to heal a mind and life. She writes:

Immediately upon the birth of my son—I felt empowered. Labor and giving birth were the first event in my life I had done entirely by myself. No one could take credit for that wonderful experience. My son was born at home with my husband and two midwives in attendance. For the majority of labor I had been alone with my husband; the midwife arrived after I had begun to push, only thirty minutes prior to the birth.

From that first second—when I took my son into my arms—I knew I was a capable woman. No one else in the world could care for this child the way I could, because I knew him, because I was *me* with special things to give.

I had never felt this way before in my entire life. As a child and young adult I had literally prayed for death. I never wanted to live to be an adult. I had never wanted children. I had been slated as a perfect candidate for postnatal depression—it never happened! From the moment of his birth I knew it wouldn't happen.

My pregnancy was a time of fear and joy for me. The previous three years of my life had been riddled with the loneliness and uncertainty of mental illness. What had started as memory lapses and anxiety attacks had become psychotic episodes followed by long bouts of depression.

I was excited to learn I was pregnant but knew I would be unable to care for a baby due to my mental condition. I was in counseling at the time and my counselor agreed that, without a lot of help

161

(childcare, support and so forth) I probably would not be able to give proper care to someone as needy as a newborn baby. In fact there was some doubt as to whether or not the stress of labor would send me into a psychotic episode, and the local psychiatric emergency services were notified and supplied with my case history so they could be on the alert as my due date approached.

About halfway through the pregnancy I got sick and tired of my so-called "support" people (including an adoption counselor), and in my anger, and fear of losing control, I decided to keep the baby. I instinctively knew I could handle labor. I still had my doubts about childcare. I expected motherhood, at least during Owen's infancy, to be a horrible task to be endured.

I told my husband, who seemed to resent me and the pregnancy, that he'd better change his attitude or I would leave. This was an incredible thing for me to say since I was housebound due to anxiety and never went anywhere without him.

The closer I got to my due date the more instinctual I felt about things. Every now and then a rush of confidence and wisdom would come over me. Suddenly in the midst of uncertainty I would know the way—almost know the future, not specific events, but in a general way that left me feeling confident and peaceful. My relationship with my husband improved and we became very "in tune."

Labor was all I hoped it would be (not expected—I was at a total loss and didn't know what to expect). I was amazed by the intensity of pain. I never knew pain like that existed—like a solid dark green inescapable cloud. I didn't scream because it wasn't a red screaming sort of pain. It was just so immense I sort of mentally sat back and watched it roar over me. The birth was great—I loved pushing, I loved feeling him heavy between my legs—my bottom remembers the great feel as he came out—spectacular!

I never expected to feel so touched. It was amazing and wonderful to see him being born, and to feel that pulsating cord—almost addictive—like I want to feel it again and it would be worth everything before and after. I think women are really honored and lucky to be able to experience it.

I loved the baby and wanted him and was surprised by how much I felt like I knew him. We were old friends already Owen and I.

I felt capable, in control and wise. I felt very wise as if the power of every woman—every mother since the beginning of time—were suddenly mine. Instead of feeling like me against the world I felt like part of the eternal sorority of motherhood/womanhood.

Though I had never cared for a baby in my life (not even babysitting), I wasn't nervous. I felt so able to care for him and to know that if something was truly wrong I would know. I felt in touch with the baby—and with reality, more than I had in years.

Despite Linette's new confidence, all did not go smoothly at first:

We had great difficulty getting the baby to nurse during the first few days after his birth. Women from La Leche League came over, midwives came over—all trying to force the baby to nurse. I was hysterical, not out of fear for the baby, but because I knew what they were doing was wrong. I told everyone to leave the two of us alone—we could work it out. They didn't believe it. At the insistence of my husband and midwife we took the child to another woman to be nursed. I was filled with anger and resentment—again my "support" people were telling me I couldn't do it.

Late that night, alone with my hysterical hungry baby, we worked it out—not by force, not by trickery, not by giving my child to another woman. I did it. I knew my baby. I knew that all we needed was quiet time alone. (I need to add that while everyone was telling me I couldn't do it, the woman who nursed my baby was the one person who reassured me that I could—she told me I was a beautiful powerful woman. Her son was born about one hour after mine. It seems both of us new mothers were able to see and feel that capability.)

I shouldn't blame people for doubting my abilities—I had doubted them, too. There was no way to explain to them the new person I had become. That suddenly I knew it was going to be okay—be better than okay.

This is not to say those first weeks were easy. I was dizzy with lack of sleep and there were times in the wee hours that I wished the baby had never been born. But somehow I was able (which I never was before) to know that this difficult period would pass. Prior to my son's birth, when I felt down my thoughts went to suicide—not overcoming.

My life has changed—my awareness of myself and the world has changed since the birth of my son. My problems have not disappeared entirely. I am still in counseling. I still hallucinate and go through periods of depression. I am still prone to unexplainable and sudden mood swings. But I have not attempted suicide or slashed my body up since Owen was born. I no longer pray for death. I am able to ask for help when I need it—a sign that I want to, and believe I am able to "get better."

I rarely venture out of the house alone and I still shy away from social interaction but slowly and in subtle ways I am reaching out. In little ways I am making myself heard.

I think it's important to explain that I never felt my son to be an extension of me. Owen is as separate an individual as anyone else in my life. I was empowered by the labor and birth and, I'm sure, by my daily interaction with him—but he is not responsible for that. If, heaven forbid, I were to lose my son, I believe I would still retain what I've gained by having him. In many ways I've come to life since he was born, but Owen is not my life nor am I living through him. We are separate people, there are things we do together and things we do apart—and I am better able to do my own things, now. (Of course I have less time for "my things" but the time I have is, for the most part, more productive and my work is of higher quality.)

I've asked Linette what she thinks may have been the cause of these profound changes in herself. Her reply:

In some part I think it's due to my making decisions for myself and having the strength to see them through against adversity. Part I feel is due to God rendering a change in me—answering prayers of years—and, as He promises, giving me the strength to get through what He asks of me.

And also I believe in raw instinct and certain natural forces—the life force and being so close to it during pregnancy—very powerful stuff.

"There have been other changes too," Linette adds. "They may seem less dramatic—but they have been life changing to me just the same":

I have learned to appreciate each moment, each experience. I used to complain about and negate any part of my life that wasn't pleasing. Now I don't do that—I've learned that it's all part of my life and I can either wish it away or allow myself to experience it. Instead of complaining or grinning and bearing it—I let myself feel.

When the baby gets me out of bed at one A.M.—I feel; then instead of wishing away this moment of my life, and his—I live it. We do something together, or he plays while I write or draw. Sure I'm tired—but it's my life, and I don't want to waste it. And surprisingly enough those old zombie, complaining hours have become productive and often memorable hours.

Life does not shut down between midnight and seven A.M.—life does not become useless when the baby's crying. It still exists and deserves to be lived. That awareness came to me during the early weeks after my son's birth—as I crawled out of bed I realized I was wasting so much time and opportunity to be with my little baby, trying to get him to sleep while he was wide awake, fighting instead of loving, resisting instead of living.

Caring for him became so much easier when I let it. Suddenly life became very crystalline instead of a hazy blur. I carry beautiful details like gems in my pocket. My son isn't growing up too fast because I've lived it along with him. I haven't wished away his infancy, or my motherhood—not even the hard times, the way I used to wish away weeks, even years of my life.

If that's not altered awareness—I don't know what is.

Part IV

OTHER DOORS
OF
AWARENESS

13

Seeing Around Corners

*M*any stories of the newborn year involve psychic and intuitive experiences. There are moments when we seem to see around corners of time and space, sense hidden dimensions of the world, or bridge the separateness of persons.

Though the words "psychic" and "intuitive" are often used as synonyms, there is an important difference. Intuition is a shortcut in thinking. It's an educated guess, where the process is outside awareness but still quite rational. It draws on everything we know but are not aware of, such as sensory messages we register unconsciously, and all the information we've "forgotten." A psychic perception is more mysterious, for there is no inner or outer source of information we can identify. It is as though another sense has opened.

Because our fives senses do extend beyond the limits of consciousness and feed directly into intuitive "flashes," it's often hard to tell whether an impression is psychic or intuitive. A mother recalls:

> When my baby was born, we lived in a town where we knew hundreds of people. One day in the first week after his birth, the thought of a certain acquaintance came into my mind just seconds before she knocked on the door. The clarity of my perception startled me and felt extra-sensory, but I can't rule out the possibility that unconsciously I heard and recognized her footstep or even caught her scent!

Through whatever channels, an early warning system seems to operate during newborn time, increasing our sensitivity to people and situations impinging on the nest: "I always knew who was calling on the phone."

"In the days and nights in the hospital following the birth," Sue Akerman writes, "there were some things significantly unusual for me occurring. Example—my friend Shannon appearing one afternoon unannounced, while I was thinking about her. I had not seen or heard from her for more than a year. This was very moving for me—and a more pronounced example of that sort of thing than at other times in my life."

Holly Piper took her baby along to the theater one day. Before the film started:

> I was watching the people coming in and the general bustle. I noticed a man who wasn't doing anything in particular and then a dark thought crossed my mind. I worried, "What if there was a fire here—how would I get Emma out." Then I felt like it would be okay. The movie started and after we were about an hour into it Emma was getting restless so I took her out into the hallway. I noticed people bustling and then there were fire engines and trucks outside of the theater. Someone had pulled the alarm. When we went back into the theater the man I'd noticed earlier was up on the stage making an announcement—not to worry, it was a false alarm . . .

Was this just the anxiety of a new mother, scanning an environment for the first time in terms of her baby's safety? Or was Holly seeing around a corner of time into the future?

Time's usual boundaries are a little less fixed, to our awareness after childbirth. In many stories it seems as though past and future are interleaved with the present. One woman, heading into an exhausted depression, found herself "in an altered state where all levels of time and space occurred simultaneously." Much less frightening are the fleeting "double exposures" like Linda's experience during the first week after childbirth:

> One night I dozed off and was in a half awake, half asleep state, dreaming of a strange woman. I thought I heard the phone ring twice and my husband answer hello. Then I woke up and went into the other room. When I asked David who was on the phone, he said the phone didn't ring. Then he came to bed and we began to chat. This time the phone really rang twice and he said hello—it was a strange woman making a prank phone call.

Jill similarly experienced a split-level moment of time, with a future event superimposed on the present:

> Nathan (my first child) was born in January 1983. The morning after his birth, I was waiting for the nurse to bring him for his morning feeding when I saw a "vision" that I would be in the same room a year later with another baby. The baby that the nurse was holding out to me in the vision was longer, thinner, with darker hair, redder skin. Now I was peculiarly puzzled by this vision as I had seen Nathan the night before, who had light brown hair and soft clear skin covered with downy hair. The vision vanished when the maternity nurse brought Nathan in.
>
> Over the next few months I was busy with Nathan and quite

forgot about the vision. In May I knew I was pregnant again. Our second boy was born in March. After his delivery I was scheduled for a tubal ligation. After leaving the recovery room they took me to the maternity ward. They brought me to the same room and the same bed I had when I delivered Nathan over a year earlier. When the nurse brought Aaron in at two A.M. it was the same vision that I had the year before. Aaron was longer and appeared much thinner than Nathan did. He was also very red and dry from the difficult delivery.

We've seen how emotions from the past may flood into awareness. Time seems to open up in other ways, bringing lost memories and reveries that link us with distant times. Pat Turgon writes:

Jesse was born with the first pink lights of dawn, and throughout that day I had flashes of union and similarity with women everywhere . . . That first night the sense of commonness to mothers since time immemorial was particularly strong. I had flashes of tending babes at different times throughout history, which makes me now wonder if they were past life visions because they were so real and clear even though only for a moment. I experienced the emotion of the particular moment in time that I was tuning in to, and the sounds, smells, textures of the scene.

Colleen Waddell enjoyed similar feelings in the weeks after her second child's birth, and says, "I cherish them so and hope never to lose them entirely." A midwife herself, Colleen found ways to preserve the special awareness, and suggests, "Be selfish with yourselves and your time with your new baby. Follow your deep intuitions. Forget the rest of the world." She writes:

I felt connected with my daughter as well as all women throughout time. All the women before us and all the women after us. I could clearly remember what it was like to be a newborn, and the changes I felt as I integrated mySELF to the newborn's existence.

This was real intense. I did all I could to preserve it because I was experiencing it as very positive. I didn't leave my room, change my clothes, comb my hair, didn't wipe off my baby. I ate very little and very pure. I was able to share a great deal with my husband because he was out of work and home all the time. This made it easy for me to isolate myself and my family and extend this experience. I experienced flashbacks of myself and other women birthing as well as being born, over long periods of time.

"For several months after my middle child's birth," says Diane Gregg,

"I kept having spontaneous past-life flashbacks that were quite amazing. They fit together some pieces in my life, especially childhood, so well that I had to believe they have basis beyond imagination."

Diane is a midwife who encourages pregnant couples to develop psychic awareness. In an article published in *Mothering* magazine, she writes:

> Anyone who has been pregnant or been intimate with pregnant women realizes the altered state of consciousness that characterizes pregnancy and also the breastfeeding relationship. This altered consciousness, this increased sensitivity to both internal and external environments, can facilitate growth and increase psychic abilities . . .
>
> Psychic awareness enhances knowledge of the fetus's condition from conception on and can alert the woman to special stresses or a need for change. It can be used to initiate bonding during pregnancy and to get to know the soul before birth.

How can one distinguish between accurate information and the projection of our own fears and hopes? Diane says:

> How to tell the difference is certainly a challenge. I encourage people to trust and act on those little impulses we all get so they can get a feel for the process and learn to trust their inner voice. In my experience, the more you listen and invite the inner guidance to be known to you, the more it works.

Many people do feel they have become more psychic or intuitive through the changes of birth and the newborn year. Some speak of becoming aware of their intuition and trusting it more. Others notice a new sensitivity to subtle perceptions: "I look at people and know a little more than they say. In empty rooms I get impressions of things which may have happened there."

Says Carla Sunderland, "Since her birth, I have noticed a difference in myself. I can see auras around people better than before." Another woman mentions that from the day of their daughter's birth both she and her husband have had an increase in psychic experiences.

Why does the coming of a child favor these alternate channels of awareness? Perhaps they are part of the streamlining of our attention for efficient baby care. Conscious thinking tends to be both cumbersome and too speedy; it hurries past the simplest solution and gets lost in speculation. Meanwhile, the unconscious reasoning process that we call intuition goes straight for the best bet. During the newborn year we analyze less, and let our intuition be heard. Perhaps it's the shifting of our personal boundaries that allows consciousness to expand into other times and places.

"I think it's a combination of things," says Holly Piper. "I nursed my daughter and so I spent a lot of time sitting and lying with her. I think having quiet times like that tends to open you up for tuning in to things on the subtler levels of existence. Also I think just the intensity of giving birth affected my whole being." Holly continues:

I felt an almost spiritual reverence about her. It is that "spiritual" place where I was dwelling that seemed to allow the other things to come to me.

My actual experiences seemed to come later—maybe after three or four months. We were almost as closely connected as in those early days—maybe more so. I noticed that a lot of things were happening to me on kind of a psychic level. I started off thinking they were coincidences, but then some were stronger and it all started making sense to me. I had been cultivating my relationship with Emma in a totally nonverbal way (from her side), yet because I was tuned in, I knew her wants and needs. It must have been like an exercise to me (an unconscious one), and it opened up that level of communion with me and others close to me (and not so close).

I don't remember all the happenings—many were very subtle. Some examples would be: thinking of calling someone and having them call (this happened a lot during this time, especially with two women who were close with me who were also mothering young babes); the same would happen with letters—I have a lot of friends scattered about and sometimes I would get a strong feeling of one and sense different things (happy, sad and so forth) and usually it was in tune with something they were going through.

Then similar things happened but with more intensity. I was away for a weekend, a casual friend was pregnant but not due for a couple more weeks. One morning I started thinking of her very strongly—a couple hours later I was getting cramps that reminded me of early labor. When I went home two days later I learned that was the time she was having her baby.

There's one road that I drive on to come home to the farm; maybe this happens because it's so familiar to me, but I always know if a car is coming around a certain curve before I get to the curve, or if I should slow down because an animal might be crossing or along the road. I feel it before I see it and it's always right.

Sometimes when I'm driving or even sitting or walking I notice things out of the corners of my eyes—movements of what seem to be figures, almost elflike.

Also I've noticed that I remember many more things than I've been consciously aware of from my childhood. I've been seeing things through her eyes and recalling my parents in certain times (when I was very young) with a lot greater clarity. And I've been a lot more aware of my dreams—I remember them clearly and frequently.

It was fully three years after her baby's birth that Holly wrote: "I feel like my perceptors have been opened up. So much is going through me now since Emma's birth and I'm trying to process it all as quickly as I can. It's hard to sort out what's normal and what's unusual for me these days."

Holly points out that this opening began with that first "exercise" of non-verbal attunement to her baby. And it is here that the majority of unusual events during the newborn year occur: in the mysterious connection between parent and child.

~   ~   ~

We can often check the validity of our apparent psychic experiences and intuitions. For example, we can compare our dreams and hunches with other people's perceptions, or wait to see whether a premonition comes true in time. But by far the most frequent of these events during the newborn year are moments of feeling telepathically connected with the baby. In most cases we can't confirm that the baby's inner experience matches our impression of it, but sometimes there is some evidence to go on. For example, a mother while separated from her baby dreams of him crying; later she learns he was in distress at that moment.

The next five stories in this chapter focus on the possibility that parents can go beyond a simple attunement with their newborn, to actually connect with the baby's consciousness and sense what she is feeling or thinking.

Dené Ballantine noticed that right from the beginning she was able to distinguish her baby's crying from that of other babies, but also that she knew when her baby awoke in the nursery. Later, this attunement proved life-saving:

> I would frequently feel like I was my daughter, and feel sensations that would cause me to protect her. Once, I felt like I was unable to breathe, and rushed into her room to find her with a liner from a disposable diaper over her nose and mouth. I frequently could feel her sensations while nursing and just in general.

Cathie Morales found that her experience brought closeness and loving feelings, and "a conviction of ties" to her newborn:

> I gave birth to Louie at home. At three days of age he was jaundiced and admitted to the hospital for phototherapy. The night Louie was admitted I had the following dream: I am in a bathtub full of water, washing and soaking. I slip underwater and change into my newborn son, Louie. I am unable to get above water and as Louie, I am

crying underwater. I struggle and then I wake up.

As soon as I woke, I phoned the hospital. I heard crying in the background and the nurse on duty said Louie was fine, fed, but crying without comfort. My interpretation at the time? That I was psychically *connected* to my newborn.

Fran Vasi also feels that she shared her baby's inner world through a dream. The baby had been circumcised shortly after his birth. Fran writes:

One afternoon during his first month, I lay down with him to nap, and as he nursed I fell asleep. I had a dream. Everything was white in the dream—the place, the people were all in white. I saw no faces and I was just lying there. I remember feeling confused, I remember thinking, "Why are they going to hurt me?" and fear. Then in an abrupt moment I awoke suddenly, startled and disoriented, and my baby was crying as if something was wrong, as if he was hurt.

That was over eight years ago and I still remember the incident, the dream very clearly. I'm convinced the dream was my baby's, of his circumcision.

Communion with the baby sometimes takes the form of hearing an inner voice—even holding a "conversation" with the child. Mary Lynch recalls:

When the baby was born, we had not chosen the right name. Somehow, the names we had were not right for him. We were ready to leave the hospital and we had not settled on his name. I took a walk to the nursery window, alone, to try to understand what his name might be. I heard the name "James" whispered in my head. It came from nowhere I could pinpoint. It did not seem to come from me. We had never discussed it and it just hadn't even occurred to me. I was thinking about this and not looking at the babies and I said, "Hi, James," at the nursery window. My son opened his unseeing newborn eyes and looked at me for a minute. I just chuckled and took him back to my room. Nothing my boyfriend said could change my mind.

"Our first born, Isaac, died three days after his home birth," Margaret writes. "I was blessed with many experiences beyond ordinary consciousness during his earthly sojourn. Our second child, Jennifer, was born with Down's Syndrome and I had one rather extraordinary experience with her several hours after her birth." Here is Margaret's story of communion on other levels with both of her children.

After crowning, when Isaac's body slipped out of my own, I sensed a profound "twinkling" of energy up above my left shoulder over the bed. As the midwives raised his body over my abdomen up to my chest I could feel the absolute stillness in that lifeless little body. My attention was drawn back to the twinkling energy over the bed. I had barely touched his empty physical vessel with my hands when I handed him over for resuscitation. I knew Isaac's spirit was connected only minimally to that body—his essence was up above the bed.

I felt like I was in a vibrational cloud—I could hardly relate to the facts of what had transpired. "When I realize what's happened will you be here?" was a question I asked a midwife after Isaac had been transported to the hospital and they were attending to my torn perineum.

After I went to the hospital where I saw him attached to seemingly endless tubes and wires, I walked up to the little isolette, unable to restrain my sobbing. His ten pound body looked so small—so vulnerable—so quiet. I touched his back with the palms of my hands and immediately "heard" in what seemed like a powerful booming thought transference "Don't be deceived by appearances!!! I am much more than that form—and so are you! Remember!" I was stunned . . . And the tears went away.

Throughout his seventy-two hour life I could often feel that Isaac was somewhere else and not present with this body that I held and rocked and sang to. One time when I was feeling the drama of the situation, I felt irritated that here Sam and I were going through all of these changes and Isaac didn't even have the "decency" to be there sharing this time with us. Internally I shouted "Isaac! Where are you!?"

I was suddenly transported in consciousness to what seemed to be a round room. There was a hazy golden mist in it, and the interior of the sphere was white. I could not see bodies of people, but I sensed many presences of Spirit in this room and somehow I knew they were other souls in transition, deciding whether to remain earth bound or to move on. It was like I could feel or intuit the truth of what was happening. Isaac was indeed there, comforting and supporting others in their choices. Suddenly I could sense that my presence was noticed and I knew I did not belong. I hastily retreated in utter humility.

I tried to imagine a mother-child relationship with Isaac—I fantasized his attachment for me—but it was just not so. Oh, I felt a love from him, so pure and vital and infinite, and yet it was very impersonal. Probably the truest, most God-like love I have ever known.

Isaac's final thought transference was this, "Know that this planet is your community. The only way that you will ever be able to resolve conflict and overcome negativity is through Love, and through recognition of your true self, and that same Self who lives in each and every one of you."

I think the physical pain of labor (I never knew a body could hurt so intensely) forced me into an altered state, and the shocking reality of this transition of birth through death kept me there for his sojourn through the earth plane and for about a week afterward. It helped me to deal with the great influx of energies, at the hospital, with friends, and so on. I felt as though Spirit was my constant companion through these days, filtering energies, offering new perspectives and supporting. It slowly faded away in the course of the month and a half after he died.

Twelve hours after Jennifer's birth, a pediatrician came into our room and told us they thought she had Down's Syndrome. I could feel the blood in my head drop to my feet. I felt faint, and I had the flashing thought, "Okay—where is the window that I jump out of?"

Now Jennifer who had been so sweet and gentle up to that point was lying next to my bed on an isolette. She let out a very loud shriek immediately after I had the thought of looking for a window. I looked at her and she looked directly back at me—eyeball to eyeball—and conveyed to me distinctly in thought transference, "Mother dear, two minutes ago I was the very center of your universe, and now that this man has walked in and mentioned two little words to you, you are about to do us both in?"

Stunned (again) I realized how quickly I had betrayed her in my heart, and I picked her up with more love and admiration than I had ever known was possible for a person to feel. And we bonded again—our little family—in joy and love and tears—deeper and deeper, stronger and stronger.

My experience with Jennifer reminded me of my deepest priorities and cemented a respect for who she is that grows deeper every day. The psychic connection with her is stronger than any I have known with another person. I have come to see through the myths of "normal" and "perfection" and have been celebrating her own unique unfoldment rather than haunting her with my expectations.

From these experiences, Margaret derived "an incredible love and appreciation for this gift of life and a peace-making with the pain in life that is such a great teacher." They have reminded her, she says, "to drop my resistance and fears and to welcome the wonder and glory of life as it presents itself. There is far more here than meets the eye."

Another aspect of the psychic bond between parent and baby comes into focus here. As Jennifer apparently responded to her mother's thought, in the following stories babies seem to hear and respond to thoughts, emotions, even physical sensations of their parents. This may happen over and over, coming closer to proving a telepathic connection.

"I have always been skeptical of psychic experiences," says Leslie Burnham. "I'm pretty much a person who doesn't believe in the supernatural, at least not pertaining to me. My experiences post-adoption, however, have made me somewhat alter my views."

Leslie's adopted baby, Elizabeth, was unusually demanding, needing to be held and walked through most of her waking hours during her first nine months:

> Elizabeth did begin to sleep a lot, though. Not for more than two hours at a time, and never through the night, but I began to adjust to her schedule. I would try to straighten up the house and to find some time for myself during her naps. Sometimes I would use the time to organize her baby book and photo albums.
>
> It began to seem that every time I'd open the photo album, she'd wake up from her nap. At first I thought it was because I would look at the photo album after I had completed my household chores, and she was nearing the end of her nap time anyway, but eventually I realized that it didn't matter when I looked at the photographs. She would always wake up. Looking at photographs isn't a noisy activity, so I couldn't understand it. After a long time, I finally came to the conclusion that when I was looking at pictures of her, I was concentrating on her, and somehow she knew it and it caused her to wake up.
>
> I never told anyone, other than my husband, about this. Too many people thought I was too involved with Elizabeth as it was. But I know this happened, and I made a point of not looking at her photo albums if I wasn't ready for her to be awake (and crying as usual). This occurred from about the time she was six weeks old until she was nine months old.

Jan Hunt is a psychologist with a long-standing interest in psychic phenomena. "I spent one summer with Dr. Rhine at Duke University doing ESP research," she says. "I've had several psychic experiences myself, mostly telepathy and precognition."

Jan's story differs from the others because it involves an older baby—one old enough to talk. Her son Jason was "a `miracle baby' the doctors told us we'd never have due to infertility." During the pregnancy, Jan felt able to communicate with him: "For instance, if I hadn't felt him move for a while I'd think `Are you okay? Let me know'—and he would immediately kick strenuously." When Jason was about one year old, Jan began to notice episodes of apparent telepathy:

> At about one or one and a half, Jason was asleep, and I was awake next to him (we have a family bed). I was thinking, "He hasn't been enjoying bagels for a while, maybe I should put some jelly on it." Still asleep, Jason said, "Jelly on it, jelly on it, jelly on it." And that was the only time he's ever talked in his sleep.
>
> At eighteen months old, I had the thought, "I wonder if I should

go into town?" and Jason immediately looked at me and said, "town?"

At twenty-eight months, Marcus was thinking, "I should return our empty bottles to the store," and immediately Jason walked to the kitchen, went to the cupboard and took out all the empties—something he had never done before.

At twenty-nine months, I was awake in the morning and Jason was still asleep. I had the thought, "I wonder what cake I should make for tomorrow's meeting?" When Jason woke up a few minutes later, the first thing he said was, "Where is the cake?" I asked, "What cake?" and he replied, "for the meeting!"

At four years, he asked me several times over several days if I could "see through my nose." Finally, I asked him if he could, and he said yes, and pointed to the "third eye" area. I'm fairly certain we had never mentioned the third eye to him.

Jan notes regretfully that these episodes seem to have stopped at around age four.

Some parents discover that they can use this mind-link in a very practical way. Bunny Chidester, who felt a oneness with her new baby, found that the experience "taught me to use my mind in a way I didn't realize I could":

I feel at one with his center. There is a bond there that is so strong I can feel it all the time. I can calm him even now with my mind. I can center myself and tune into his center, and calm him immediately with my mind when he is upset.

Doris developed a skill similar to Bunny's with her own firstborn son:

Many times a day I have observed my son Kaegan—now six months old—reading my thoughts or experiencing my thoughts, feeling physical things that happen to my body, and being as sensitive to what is happening to my emotional/physical body as to his own.

In the days after he was born, whenever I thought about the birth, or tried to remember what it was like, Kaegan would instantly start crying. He would wake up from a deep sleep! I was not able to process the birth experience for myself until more than a month had passed.

I frequently daydream about "what ifs"—what would happen if that car hit us and we—or what if I fell while carrying Kaegan, or what if Dad got hurt etc. I used to daydream the scene all the way through to how the "good ending" was reached. Well, Kaegan would cry, wake up, fuss, from the instant I started this type of daydream until I stopped. I would say Kaegan was sensitive to this for two months or more. At first it would wake him; then as time went on he became less and less sensitive. For the first few months, however, I had to just stop that type of thinking. In a way I wish he was still as sensitive. I think it is healthy for me to stop this type of daydreaming.

This would also happen (it doesn't anymore) when my husband and I made love. Kaegan would instantly wake up. At first it seemed he was in tune with my feelings of unsurety—because I was still tender from the birth—as soon as I felt any anxiety Kaegan would wake up. Later however I was totally comfortable with making love and Kaegan would still wake up. It seemed as if he was still so connected to me physically that when an area of my body was touched that had given him pain he would feel it . . . as if his cells had a memory of being part of me.

(Consider this observation by an adoptive mother: "I have never given birth, but had the good fortune recently to be present at the birth of my niece. When she was a few minutes old, after I cut the cord, the baby was placed on a table while the midwife stitched the mother. I clearly saw the baby wince at the first prick of the needle!") Doris continues:

Kaegan responds surprisingly well to mental pictures. When I want to dress him, and visualize him putting his arm through a sleeve, he very often does it. Visual pictures work very well; I usually picture what I want while telling him what I want.

A week or two ago we were in the car—Kaegan was crying and fussing. I stared into his eyes, smiled and began picturing rainbow colored water falls, beautiful flowers, mountains—and he calmed down and fell asleep.

He needs a great deal of one on one mental bonding with me. He will be out of sorts and nothing will calm him, until I clear my mind and focus on the place where his mind and my mind meet. (It is a physical feeling that I get so that I know I have found the right spot in my mind.) Then he is calm and able to fall asleep—eat—whatever it is he needed to do but couldn't without my help.

Doris proposes that such communion is possible because babies are able "to see our thoughts; they do not know the difference between thoughts and reality." Noting that Kaegan's telepathic attunement to her seems to be gradually diminishing, she adds:

Babies are still part of their mothers physically, emotionally and mentally until they begin to collect enough experiences of their own to feel separate. I think my child is learning which information he collects inside his little head he should pay attention to, and what information he can let pass.

Had Doris noticed any hints of this telepathic closeness, while pregnant with Kaegan? "I did not feel very connected to my baby during pregnancy," she says—"not very connected to the spirit within me. I think it was my lack of knowledge and experience: I had no idea babies were such aware, alert, capable individuals. My next pregnancy will be very different."

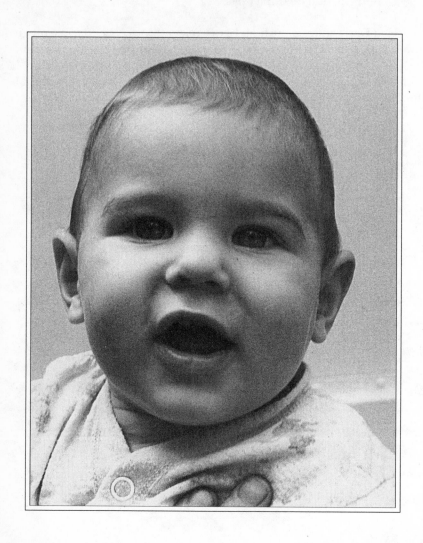

14

Dreams, Visions And Visitors

You could not say that Linda Wyatt and her first baby Simon had a smooth start together. Simon needed resuscitation at birth, and Linda, recovering from the caesarean delivery, was unable to see him until the following day. It was not an easy transition to motherhood for a young woman who says she was "very afraid about being responsible enough to be a mother." But love's ingenuity found a way to lessen her anxiety and create closeness with the baby—through dreams. Linda writes:

> Simon is the only baby I have had anything to do with. I did very little babysitting as a teen, so I started out as a completely inexperienced mother . . . and did not feel like a mother really until some time later—a little after the dreams started.
>
> Once, when I was eighteen, I had a lucid dream—where I knew I was dreaming and was in control of the dream. Starting soon after Simon and I came home from the hospital, I had more of these dreams—sometimes several days in a row. In most of them, Simon and I would be together. We would talk about things, or we would go places and he would ask me questions. I always woke up feeling very close to him. I then noticed that these dreams always occur when I am sleeping next to Simon, but not when we are in separate rooms.
>
> Simon is now almost eleven months old and I am still having these dreams. I have learned to have more and more control—I can now keep myself from waking, if I want. I have complete control over the contents of the dream, except Simon's part. I feel like he is really there—not part of the dream, but real. I can change everything else at will, but not Simon. I wish there was some way to ask him.
>
> These dreams are a lot of fun, and I think they also contribute to our close relationship. I have become more relaxed about motherhood.

When her baby was almost fifteen months old, Linda wrote again.

"Simon weaned himself a couple of weeks ago and I have not had any lucid dreams since then. This somehow makes sense to me. A couple of days ago, I bought the book *The Family Bed* (Avery Publishing Group, 1987) by Tine Thevenin and read this:

> 'Breastfeeding mothers have noticed that they will frequently awaken in the middle of the night shortly before their baby begins to whimper. Results of recent research suggest . . . that a nursing mother may awaken in anticipation of her child's cry because she and her infant dream in unison. It is suspected that the hormone, prolactin, may be the key to this mysterious link. This lasts only as long as breastfeeding is continued. With bottlefed infants and their mothers this will last only for about two weeks. After that, the mother and child have completely different and unequal sleep cycles.'"

The dreams of newborn time, like Linda's "lucid" dreams, often take place in an expanded borderland between sleep and waking. Sometimes they are pleasant and the dreamer has a sense of control, as in the following examples which also possess an intensely vivid and "real" quality. Bev Dittberner writes:

> The night after my baby's birth, I had a "dream" that I swear to this day was an out of body experience. It was so strange and real, it was like I was awake only somewhere far away and I had complete control of everything that was going on. I call it a dream because I don't know what else to call it, and I was in the same place when I got back that I was when I left, and it was during the time I must have been sleeping.
>
> I was on a beach and there were large buildings behind me and I was directing the entire "vision"—I either knew things were going to happen or I "made" them happen, that is the only thing about the experience that is not clear. Every sound, every color and shape of the waves, every pebble of sand I was in control of. It wasn't power, it was more like giving permission for things, clouds, people, winds, sky, everything to be its very best. I get emotional recalling it, it was so wonderful, so pure, and it's never happened again.

Cynthia Cournoyer had unusual dreams following her second child's birth:

> The first few nights (or any time I would sleep) after she was born I had the most vivid dreams. It wasn't that they felt real, like a real emotion, but they looked real.
>
> The best way to describe it is if you are aware of the difference between a sixteen millimeter film and a videotape on the television.

The video is more real. It jumps out at you. Well, the dreams were as if someone turned on the light. Very very bright. Almost to the point of losing its color. The images were one after the other; they didn't have a logical sequence or a story. And many of them involved fast motion. Like I was flying in a plane at about two feet off the ground! And I could look down at the ground and see the most incredible detail. Rocks and dirt and grass. Never has a dream been as vivid! Not since then either. I could even control the dream to some extent. I felt pleasure from this flying and would prolong it and steer it to other places.

One of the most mysterious dreams involves a split-level sense of time. When her baby girl was a few months old, Gerry "awoke" in her sleep one evening "to find myself and my daughter at my side seven years in the future":

I intuitively knew this was me meeting myself and proceeded to ask many questions. I was given a formula for healing and advice on clearing up past relationships. It was so real I thought I was awake and not dreaming. I awoke and scribbled down everything I could recall.

Meanwhile, nightmares with a theme of danger and loss abound, perhaps enacting our fears and ambivalence about the new responsibility: "Uneasy dreams of forgetting the baby or of someone taking him from me." In addition, the hormonal surges that accompany the beginning of lactation can trigger some of the same physical feelings we associate with danger. Our dreaming mind promptly invents a story to account for these alarming sensations, contributing to the vivid nightmares of the first week.

Anara Williams, a mother of two sons, had dreams of danger to a baby, but curiously enough a baby of the opposite sex. "I had several dreams of losing a baby girl—down holes and wells, under water—in the first few days after a boy was born. I needed to let go of my desire for a girl so that I could truly love and accept the boy I received."

Susie Helme recalls:

During Maya's infancy I had many nightmares about her being put by other people into a fire, wrapped up in something. Once, she was a log and someone was putting her on a fire. She was crying and I was sitting there telling her it was good for her to cry. Once she was inside a chicken with her head sticking out and some people were putting her in a wood stove, wondering how long she would need to cook.

Susie feels these dreams may reflect a tendency to project herself too much on her daughter and be overly concerned about her problems. Or, she suggests, "it could be that when we first have a baby we have difficulty conceiving of it as a human being, so I had dreams of Maya being a little piece of meat, being put into the fire." Perhaps it is significant too that Maya's arrival meant giving up her career—a sacrifice that for many women involves an anxiety like Susie's, "that stopping work would mean I'd end up being a housewife forever."

Susie's attitude toward dreams, even nightmares, is interesting. She says, "I have very upsetting dreams about my children a lot of the time, but I think it's a good thing. My dreams are trying to shock me into realizing something that my consciousness is being too rigid to recognize. I tend to get set rigidly in one way of doing things. The compensatory nature of dreams often opens my eyes."

Something of Susie's background is needed to understand a dream series in which she lived a relationship with a child who had not been born. She is a mother of two, a girl almost six and a boy one and a half. Married to a Japanese man, she has lived in Paris for five years, having lived before that in Japan for seven. "During both of my pregnancies," she says, "and a pregnancy I had earlier which I heartbreakingly had aborted, I have had fabulous dreams."

> Then, just after the birth of my daughter, I had several very vivid dreams about the baby I had aborted. They happened three nights in a row while I was in the clinic. I dreamed that I took the baby home from the hospital, and there was another child there, a boy about six or seven.
>
> I asked the person with me if I had had a child before Maya. The boy was shy and covered the bottom half of his face teasingly with his turtleneck, and I kept bugging him to tell me whether he looked like me or Hiroyuki. He finally uncovered his face a little, and told me in Japanese, "I look like Suji (my name in Japanese)."
>
> He was a real Japanese farmer-boy type boy, with apple red cheeks and cheap-looking brown knit clothes. His personality in all my dreams about him (even one I had years later where he was about twenty-three) is that of a little philosopher, the type of child that hangs around grown-ups all the time, my little companion. Knows just how to take care of mommy, but never lets it be a burden on him, very affectionate and easy-going.
>
> In that dream, I asked my companion how many years' difference there was between him and Maya, and she said three (even though he appeared to be six or seven in the dream). As I woke up, it hit me that my first baby was aborted on Christmas day, exactly three years before Maya's due date.

~ ~ ~

In many cultures there exists a belief that babies are especially close to the spirit world. Perhaps it arises from the uncanny experiences parents have in the newborn year. There are events so bizarre they seem to be the visitations of another reality. They suggest the presence of other worlds overlapping ours and sometimes filtering through—or do they simply reveal the projective powers of our own minds?

However harmless these visitations appear, they can be disturbing—particularly for someone as rational and down to earth as Peggy describes herself:

> I'm very practical, organized, stubborn, proud to be a "thinker." Love my husband and love my kids. I love my gardens, they are beautiful, productive, amazing! I would hate to work outside my home. Am nervous, fast, compulsive about "doing things," moody, set in my ways, like to see all sides of an issue.
>
> I had a real strange experience when my first child was three months old. This was four years ago but it is still very clear in my mind. I am curious to know if others have had experiences near to mine. I am not very `open' to such phenomena and have never had such an experience either before or after this one, but this sure was "real."
>
> November 17, 1982. Leo is three months old. He is a huge baby, very wakeful at night. I am down on the couch and he is in the cradle next to me. My husband is upstairs sleeping. I had been nursing and rocking the baby and he was finally asleep. I think I was asleep or almost asleep. I sat up and saw the room was light.
>
> There was a very bright white light form directly over Leo. It stayed there until I started screaming. I switched on the light—Greg ran downstairs and I told him I saw a ghost. I was not afraid it would hurt me or Leo, only afraid because I did not understand it. I shook for hours. Leo woke up at my screams but was not distressed.
>
> It stayed very big on my mind for many months. I talked to friends about it, who had many different ideas on what it was I experienced. I still don't know. I still run through that room at night to get to the switch.

At the time, Peggy says, she interpreted the vision as "a ghost, or visitor, that had something to do with my baby." But she acknowledges that exhaustion and emotional conflicts may have played a part, and adds, "I am still puzzled."

Deborah and Charles Prince also sensed visitors in the house after their baby's birth:

> After Shawn was born we felt the presence of angels daily, for about three months. Sometimes it was so strong we'd get up to see "who" was in the house. It was hard for me to go into another room alone late at night because the presence was so strong—it sent chills up and down my spine. Shawn seemed to be aware of their presence also. Charles says he saw a lot of white light "auras" in our house during that time.

Although many people encounter presences that seem unfriendly, the Princes readily identify their visitors as angels. Deborah explains:

> As far as knowing whether our visitations were angelic—two years before conception, we received an unsolicited education on the difference between evil and good spiritual presences, so we knew how to recognize them: ie. white, gold, violet or blue light as good—dark, green or red light as evil—and also other indicators.
>
> In preparation for conception and birth and afterwards, we did a lot of purification of ourselves and our home with prayer, white candles, pure incense, soft music.
>
> May I offer an explanation as to why most people perceive their visitations as evil? Most people are taught such things do not exist—unless they are evil. Most Christians are taught that angelic visitations are not to be expected. Ironic, considering that the Bible is full of such experiences. Also, fear tends to cloud our perceptions. If one doesn't understand, one may be afraid.
>
> Also, we are not taught the truth—that each new soul coming into this world should be regarded as precious and angelic and treated as such. That each soul receives special help from angelic sources, and that those "guides" remain with us throughout our lives.

Anne Provenzo underwent a traumatic delivery in which she felt close to death. "After this birth trauma," she says, "I definitely went through new and deeper spiritual experiences, many of which seemed to be a form of `protection' for the baby and on a lesser level, myself. This really threw me, and confirmed for me how close I had been to that `other world' during my labor." She goes on:

> As a writer, I have always been sensitive to mood, shifting colors, emotions, the stirrings of life about me—but to actually start "seeing" people—wow, that was a new one! I have "seen" people since the birth. One time, a woman passed through me at two in the

morning and she was so real that the dog went nuts. She had been standing near the crib. A week later we found out there was a gas leak under the crib.

Anne notes that although these perceptions seem to come "out of the blue," they are more apt to occur during periods of emotional stress or tension.

One of the perils of newborn time is a tendency to slip from normal sleep into a weird area of consciousness between dreaming and waking sometimes called the "half-astral plane." In this grey and often unpleasant area, visionary forms may appear. Here, Susan encountered some unexpected visitors to her new baby:

I had two unusual experiences with the birth of my two children. The experiences may have been dreams, although hallucination might be a closer name if they were really illusory events. At any rate they were extremely vivid and un-dreamlike.

The first took place a day or two after my first baby, a girl, was born in 1980. My birth was natural, undrugged and unmedicated though it did take place in a hospital birthing room. We were home within a day of the birth. The event was short and occurred as follows.

Around nine A.M. I was alone in our bedroom with the baby in her bassinet about four or five feet away. My husband had gone on to work. It was a heavily shaded room and quite grey even at that hour of the morning. I awakened with a start when I heard vague muffled mutterings of several men, three or four, whose backs were to me, bending over the baby. They were in heavy overcoats which made their shapes indistinct and as I said the light was quite dim. I have the sense that they were men but I couldn't swear that a female was not among them. They were quite middle-aged in the way of aunts and uncles vaguely known to always be present at family reunions, weddings and funerals and such. In fact, that is what they seemed to be—benign and interested relatives drawn to the presence of the new baby in the family.

However, that did not make it any less startling to find them there where I thought I was alone—very frightening at the moment. I look back on it now in a mood of calmness with the feeling that their presence, their visitation, was benign.

At the moment, however, my reaction was one of controlled panic. Their quiet whispering and their silent, unannounced entry into the room signaled to me that they wished to be unobserved and believed themselves to be. I shut my eyes quickly before they realized I was awake, to collect my thoughts and see if I could get a quick indication of what was going on—who they were, their intentions.

As soon as I did so, the room felt empty again. I lay rigid, listening for any rustling of clothing or footsteps. There wasn't the slightest sound and when I slowly opened my eyes the room was empty except for me and the baby. I lay there with my eyes open, my heart pounding, afraid to move for several minutes before I realized that whatever had happened was over.

I have puzzled over this event and told no one except my husband and now you. I only know that it was vividly, sensorily real to me.

"The second event," Susan continues, "is not so benign and makes me uneasy even now . . ."

My second baby was born in a birthing center with no medications or drugs. We were home within twelve hours. Although the labor was short (one hour) it was more painful than the first and I was in intense pain for several hours after, though there was no unusual tearing or complications. Somehow the immediate euphoria of my first birth never happened. I do not know if this set the stage for what happened next or not.

About five or six hours after we got home it was bedtime again and we were, of course, exhausted from the previous night's birth. My three-year-old was in her usual place between me and my husband in the family bed. The new baby was beside me on the floor in her little basket with a lambskin.

We were in a new house at the top of a ridge in an ordinary subdivision. When the strong thunderstorm broke with high winds it was startling, and I realized that it was the first storm since we had moved into this house.

I was awakened by a tingling, eerie physical sensation. Even in my confused state I recalled reading that many victims of a lightning strike remember experiencing an eerie tingling seconds before the bolt hit them. Well, of course, it didn't happen that we were struck by lightning but I am left with the possibility that the event was a genuine natural phenomenon connected to the intense electrical storm outside. In fact, I call this experience my "electrical dream."

I was nearly paralyzed in that state between sleep and wakefulness while the tingling grew more intense. By then I was floating about six inches above the bed and feared that I could float away entirely if I moved suddenly. I tried to moor myself by getting a grip on the mattress covering and sheets. With the greatest of efforts I moved my head to look over at my husband. He was quite asleep, though he too was suspended six inches or so above the mattress. One of his arms kept lifting up straight as though floating or pulled by a puppet string.

In that quiet, logical place in the mind that seems to keep ticking away in even the most panicky moments, I recalled that the slightest projection could attract lightning under the proper circumstances. I reached over and by excruciating concentration and effort was able to direct my arm over to his arm and push it back down. The actual push took very little effort though his arm immediately began to float back up, seemingly threatening to draw off all that tingling energy into a single split-second burst of lightning.

As I write this, my description seems very technical, even scientific. But my sense at the time was of a great malevolence, a threatening presence that was somehow expressing itself as a huge crackling field of static electricity.

This eerie suspended state lasted for probably two minutes but seemed timeless as I experienced it. I could not catch sight of our oldest child between us. She had burrowed down to my chest level and I could not bend my head enough to see her. However, I had the sense that my one hand clutching the mattress covers and the other stretched across her to my husband served not only to guide his arm back down but to keep both of them from drifting weightlessly up to the ceiling as they slept.

It was out of the question that I might summon up enough control to roll over and turn my head to check on the baby. I simply lay there, or rather floated there, with every nerve alive, listening for any sound from her.

The event did not have a clear cut end. I drifted into a troubled uneasy sleeplike state and woke up later with the clear sense of being awake in a definitely separate state from my strange "dream" and the troubled sleep that followed.

I don't discount the possibility that these two events really were dreams. However, they were unlike any dream I have had, and I am a person who dreams frequently and vividly and I recall the exact story lines, sights and sounds of dreams.

I have never talked about this to anyone except briefly to my husband who did not regard it as anything more than any other dream. I was unable to communicate to him the depth of the two experiences. I wonder if other women have had similar experiences but feared sharing them.

"A great malevolence, a threatening presence." Why do these perceptions come readily in newborn time? Some people, like Susan, remain puzzled by their experience. Others take it to be a struggle with an adversary, and use a variety of ways to resist and overcome the danger, as Alicia's "psychic battle" with a former lover, recounted in Chapter 10.

The feeling of danger centers around ourselves or around the baby. We may sense a malevolent presence that personally threatens us, often at a time when we feel physically disconnected, not fully in control. Perhaps the shock of giving birth arouses the body/mind's dread of separation and death. Melinda writes:

> All of my children were born at home. I was single at the time of my first child's birth. I was living in the house of a family for free in exchange for watching their retarded child. The woman I was living with was divorced from her former husband, who had abused her for years. The house was in bad repair and I was sleeping in the woman's room (where she had lived and been maltreated for years and years). I had also been told that a man had died in that room.
>
> I had a very long drawn out labor which would probably have been a caesarean section in a hospital. After the birth at two in the morning, my mother and sister slept on either side of me.
>
> A couple of nights after that I was either falling asleep or awakening and I saw a vision of a man (this was like a dream in a way) who was not good. He was trying to pull me out of my body. He was saying, "I see an Indian coming out of your eyes," over and over while he was trying to pull me out (through my eyes, I surmise). I had to fight very hard to resist, he was strong and I was in a weakened state. After that incident I consciously put a white light around me before going to bed. I said a prayer also.
>
> I am not sure of the meaning of this occurrence. I have felt that I was an Indian in a previous life. I believe that a pregnant woman is very powerful. After the baby is born, his soul is no longer merged with her and she isn't as strong, both physically and spiritually.

Melinda's use of prayer and visualization seems to be an effective response to these frightening events. Alan, the father who felt "a demon trying to get in me" during sleep (Chapter 8) recommends: "The best thing to do in this case is to cry out to God—Jesus—the light to save you from this force, although the presence of mind required to do this is often lacking."

Risa, who described her pregnancy and the birth as "perfect," was unprepared for the depression that set in on the second day along with frightening dreams and perceptions.

> I felt very detached and an overwhelming sense of responsibility. Gary was driving truck at the time and the baby and I were home alone at night part of the time.
>
> For the first few weeks I recall having uneasy dreams, mostly of forgetting the baby or of someone taking him from me. A couple of times I was actually caught between physical state and dream state and the feeling was very scary. Someone, not in physical body, was trying to pull the baby away from me. It was very strong and not a

good feeling. I felt someone very angry, who wanted this person back. I don't know if this is normal when experiencing postpartum depression or not.

The baby and I were in bed one night when I felt a strong presence in the room. Something was trying to pull the baby from the room. It was a strong feeling. I was aware but unable to do anything; I felt helpless and scared. Soon the feeling or presence left. The baby was still sleeping and seemed to be unaffected by it.

Medicine recognizes this condition as "sleep paralysis." It involves waking with a sense of dread, temporarily unable to move. Vivid images may appear, like Melinda's vision of a threatening man. Such episodes are thought to occur most often when there is anxiety and stress—which could account for their frequency in newborn time. (Alan found that they virtually ceased after he began regular meditation, a practice that lessens anxiety.) The experiences are still unexplained, but perhaps knowing that they have a common pattern makes them less fearfully alien.

The sense of a menacing presence may be so strong that sleep itself seems risky. Leslie, whose baby was hospitalized for respiratory distress, recalls: "When Angus was in the hospital fighting for his life I couldn't go to sleep, particularly one night, as I somehow felt I had to keep a vigil of sorts and not go unconscious, and the thought of sleep left me feeling as though demons were just waiting to grab hold of me."

Another way of dealing with these difficulties is suggested by Ed Hand. His wife Karen feared she was losing her sanity when nightmares and strange physical sensations followed the birth of her child (Chapter 4). Ed writes:

> I have been a practicing Hermetic Magickian since 1970. I work on the astral a great deal and things often follow me home if I don't seal the portals adequately. I'm confident of my ability to prevent any damage to myself but I often forget what effects psychic activities have on others.
>
> The experience was my wife's. Shortly after our son was born, something kept grabbing and holding on to Karen's wrist. I identified it as some type of disembodied spirit, human soul or elemental, I was never able to identify exactly, but it was difficult for my wife.
>
> I performed a complete exorcism using the grimoire of St. Honorius and exorcised my wife, the bedroom and the house and then set a shield of glyphs of warding and an astral pentacle. With that, plus placing bowls of holy water (again St. Honorius) and vinegar, the manifestation was banished and never returned.

Cynthia Cournoyer chose a very different tactic to deal with the sense of threat she experienced after her second child's birth. During the first few days and nights after the birth, Cynthia had vivid dreams of flying and also "very strong emotional dreams":

> I woke up actually sobbing and very upset in many instances. The dreams were very hard to shake. They always involved my husband and/or my older daughter. I don't recall if they involved the baby or not. My family was always in some kind of danger or pain. They were definitely threatened in some way, which was a threat to me because I felt as though I was losing them. I was even hesitant about going to sleep because it would happen so consistently. I had to wake up and convince myself that they were okay.
>
> My waking state was interesting also. I felt an evil presence, describing it the best way I can. It scared me a little like when you have just seen a scary movie and you are a little hesitant to go to the dark bathroom by yourself! Well, for a few days after the birth, this is how I felt. I truly did not want to be alone. I felt that this presence was also a threat to me and my family.
>
> Because of my religious beliefs, I was able to cope with this quite well. I felt the pull and the potential to really come unglued, but felt strong enough that this would not happen.

Cynthia describes her way of dealing with this unwelcome presence. "I felt that my baby needed my help or protection from these demons also. But I figured that if I didn't become emotionally involved in them and get afraid, they would give up and leave us alone. In other words, if I didn't engage in the battle, I would win by default. (Or do you say they would lose by default?)" She adds:

> Again, I think about how vulnerable the pregnant and laboring and newly-birthed mom is. So I address my situation in a more spiritual way. I believe in God and that there is good and evil in this world. I think that the "evil" acts on vulnerable people, weak in body and soul. And *that* I was. "It" takes its opportunity to confuse and drive beyond reason in the souls of those most likely to succumb.
>
> So I figure this is what was happening. By giving me the impression that my family was in danger, it weakened me further, by acting on my tender emotions. Losing sense of reality. Because in reality everything was fine. We handled the real threat to health and well being. We remained calm and acted reasonably. Our emotions were put on hold until the danger was passed. Because we handled everything so well and we were so relieved that things didn't go lousy, we found we had no real need for many of the emotions we thought we would have to experience because the birth was not perfect.

Besides the sense of personal danger, there is often a fear of losing the baby, as in Risa's perception of "someone very angry who wanted this person back." Such a fear appears in dreams and in emotional reactions like Sue Akerman's:

> I recall some strong feelings of what might be labelled "paranoia," while in the hospital. Nurses and other staff people kept coming in and wanting to take Adrian out for various reasons (weigh, photograph, etc.). I remember being adamant about keeping him with me, until I began having nightmares about the nursery, just across the hall.

Donna Kurtz's struggle for her baby took place in a dream. She writes:

> The occurrence that sticks in my head, happened the week after I had my third child—my second son. His Apgars were eight and nine because of his poor color, and he tended to bluishness sometimes. When the pediatrician checked him, I specifically asked about his heart. Doctor said it sounded fine. When Gunther was about five days old he was sleeping with my husband and me and I dreamed that the devil came up from under the bed and grabbed the baby. (I don't believe in "the Devil" or a personality called Satan.) I clutched the baby to me and imagined a white light around me and recited the Lord's Prayer over and over and over. We struggled for the baby and I won, and the devil disappeared. As I became conscious I realized what I was doing and why and continued until the feelings passed. I was wide awake and totally aware of what had happened when it was all over.
>
> Two days later the baby had a cardiac arrest at home and his heart had stopped by the time we got him to the Emergency Room. But he revived. He needed surgery, but I knew the outcome because of the outcome of the dream.
>
> Today he is nineteen months old, and a ball of fire. He's a little lover, and no one would ever imagine he's a cardiac patient!

There are various ways to think about the sense of threat that so many parents feel during newborn time. For example, one of the metabolic changes after childbirth is a drop in thyroid hormone. In *The New Mother Syndrome* by Carol Dix, a woman describes her experience when thyroid surgery had suddenly altered her metabolic state. Her words are familiar:

> I was convinced the room was filled with an electrical charge, that I was an evil spirit, that the furniture was hostile to me. I fled downstairs, shaking, and tried to pull myself together. I had never experienced hallucinations or been delirious at any time in my life,

and was consequently horrified by the strength of those feelings . . . It was as though something was taking me over from within.

A psychoanalyst, on the other hand, might suggest that these dreams and fears of losing the baby are projected from a part of ourselves that wishes someone would come and take the burden away. For as Risa commented, "motherhood is an overwhelming responsibility which I never realized." We've told ourselves in myth and fairy tale and spiritual tradition that ambivalence is dangerous—that we will lose all if we can't give our hearts completely. Yet ambivalence is always present, scaring us from within.

It's also possible that mischievous or downright malevolent entities are pestering us in our vulnerable times. If so, we may have to take seriously the advice of Karen (whose husband employed glyphs and holy water against an unwelcome presence): "Always have an exorcist available after a birth."

~　　~　　~

Gathering other people's stories, I discovered that the connection to grandparents is a recurring theme. Though long departed, grandparents often play a special role in newborn time, suggesting that our babies may have more than just distant genetic ties to them.

During both of my pregnancies, I felt close to the grandparents I had known best, lapped in a waking dream of them and their house and garden, roses, plum-trees, vine-shadowed summerhouse where Grandfather wrote his poetry. It was as if a part of me craved and lived in their remembered atmosphere.

I wondered whether my grandparents might be returning as my children, but rebirth is an open question to me and I didn't take my thoughts too seriously. Rather they seemed another expression of the closeness and continuity I felt while pregnant and for some time after the births. As the memories receded, and my grandparents' world no longer seemed to overlay mine like a golden patina, I ceased identifying the babies with them. But some parents do develop quite definite ideas as to "who" their new babies might be.

Leslie's story begins with intimations long before the birth. She was the mother of a seven-year-old boy when she sensed "a compulsion towards another pregnancy and child":

> From my very first intuitions of pregnancy, Angus seemed to make a very strong presence known. I craved protein and felt as if my body held a being with more energy than I could contain. Several times I walked two miles just to try to relieve myself of this incredible feeling of energy. As the months progressed this physical intensity subsided.

During her pregnancy Leslie had many vivid dreams about the baby:

> I dreamed: I am looking down onto a scene as if getting a bird's-eye view. I see myself taking care of a baby boy. I then hear a man's voice say to me, "Remember, when you are taking care of me, that you already know who I am." Of course I was quite excited by such a revelation and found it quite wonderful.
>
> The last dream I had was in response to my bedtime request one night. As I went to sleep a few days before I actually began labor, I said, "If I already know who you are, who are you?" I dreamed of my grandfather looking at me and laughingly saying, "You and I have a lot in common." Well, that was just more excitement than I could stand, as nothing seemed to have devastated me more in my life, and for few conscious reasons, than the death of my grandfather when I was thirteen.

Leslie had accepted the idea of reincarnation fifteen years before these events. "As long as I have known about it, it's made sense," she says. "I had always secretly hoped and felt that someday my child would be my grandfather and that the gap that had been made with his passing would be made whole again. I realized it was probably wishful thinking, but the fact that my husband has a number of skills and interests similar to my grandfather's made me dream more that this would be such a conducive environment for his personality." She continues:

> Angus was born five weeks early, within a day or two of my grandfather's date of death. My grandfather had died on a respirator, a victim of myasthenia gravis.
>
> Now that this was my second time I felt like a pro. I wanted to do everything the way I had wanted to originally but lacked confidence when Matthew was born to me at twenty-one. I put my new baby to my breast and began to realize that he seemed awfully sleepy. The pediatrician took him off to be examined and a few minutes later informed us that he was having trouble breathing.
>
> From that moment on the shock, agony and emotional pain were more than I hope I ever have to bear again. He labored on his own for almost twelve hours and finally had to be put on a respirator. When he was not a day old and I had not yet even really held him, he was airlifted to the state's Newborn Intensive Care Unit.
>
> The next week was moment to moment living not knowing whether he would live or die. Because he kept fighting the ventilator he had to be paralyzed. We were with him constantly, stroking him, talking to him and winding up a musical toy that I had a couple of times put up to my abdomen when he was especially active and rocked him to sleep with this music. We hoped he would

recognize it on some level of awareness and that it might offer him some comfort.

Finally on the seventh day I was able to hold and nurse my darling baby. He has just recently had his first bonafide sickness in two years. He talks in full sentences and doesn't seem to have been too set back by the trauma of his first couple of weeks in this world.

I find myself daydreaming more and reminiscing about the times visiting my grandparents. Angus loves to wear hats and when I was a girl I used to always call men who wore hats "grandpas" as my Grandpa wore one. I think Angus looks like a picture I have of my grandfather at twelve, too. One day he looked at me in a very funny way as if to say "I remember you." He gives me great comfort and happiness, and whether imagined or not, I find the gap now closed that I had lived with all these years after my Grandpa died.

Sheryl Newland's attitude toward reincarnation dates back to an experience in her childhood:

When I was seven and my sister was four, she died of appendicitis. A year and a half later my mother had a baby, a boy. The next year she had another boy. When my aunt (her sister) held this new baby for the first time, she got goose bumps all over and a feeling of energy going up her back. She quickly handed him back, saying that she thought he was my sister reincarnated. All this from a woman who didn't previously believe in reincarnation! She didn't know how to explain it or what it meant.

Growing up with this family story may have set the stage for Sheryl's experience with her second child. Her grandfather had died seven years before the baby's arrival. "He and I were very close," she says. "Since his death I've experienced feelings that his presence was with me. I've known him in my dreams and felt his guidance in decisions pertaining to my life." She continues:

A few hours after my son's birth I was staring at my new little being. He was the carbon copy of his father and his father before him. Suddenly his facial expressions turned into those of my grandfather. Not as an old man, but as a young man. I immediately got goose bumps all over, and the sensation that energy was shooting up my spine.

I was elated, feeling my grandfather's presence. It lasted only five to ten minutes but I never forgot it. As soon as it was over my son fell asleep.

Later, when my husband came in and gave him his middle name (Cameron) I was touched. I felt as if he must be my grandfather reincarnated. Cameron is my middle name and also that of my mother and grandfather and his mother's maiden name. There must be some connection regarding this name as each person who has had it has had a special relationship with others who have it also.

In the story of Martha Iris Cancel and her firstborn son, the baby's name is again significant. Iris is of Puerto Rican and Catholic background, her husband is Jewish, and together they attend meetings based on the teachings of Edgar Cayce, which include the concept of reincarnation:

It was my son's fifth day of life. I had been a little harried the days before because he had a high bilirubin count and the doctor had asked us to put him under the lights. We had rented lights and brought them into our bedroom. La Leche suggested that I nurse him almost constantly and so I did.

Throughout it all I had an inner peaceful feeling that told me nothing was really wrong. Now, it was all over and I took him into my arms to nurse him. As I looked down at him I saw the face of an old man, a very old man who was filled with wisdom and filled with deep, deep love. I knew he was a very kind man and I thought to myself that he understands everything and I need not worry about him. The next second I saw my baby again and I thought to myself surprised—"But Iris, what are you thinking?—he is only a baby!" And it was at that point that I realized what I had seen.

I also had the distinct impression that I knew this old man and that I loved him very much. However, when I tried to figure out who he may have been I was at a loss. Could he be someone from my past life? The only "old man" that I knew and loved very much in this life was my husband's grandfather who died over six years ago. He was a very kind man and very intelligent and probably wise but I wasn't sure if it was he or not.

In the Jewish custom, parents name their child after some loved one who has died in order to allow that soul to leave limbo and go to heaven. According to Edgar Cayce, the soul or spirit of a new baby may enter the physical body anytime after the birth—maybe a day or two or even four or five days later. That evening my husband told me that he had told his mother we would give our son the name of my husband's grandfather as his Jewish name. I remembered my "vision" and wondered if it was at the moment of his decision that Gramp's spirit had entered my son's body and if the "old man" I saw was his spirit. I wasn't sure—but it's a nice thought!

Perhaps we identify a newborn with someone already known to us so that we may heal an old loss, or make a bridge from familiar to new love and feel a deeper kinship with the baby. Perhaps we like to think the baby is old and wise because it reassures us and relieves the anxiety of being in charge. And we would naturally think of our grandparents, since they are often the ones we have lost by the time we have our own children.

Grandparents are also the ones who stand for continuity. Through our connection with them, we first understand the lineage of family past and future. We feel close to them again when we become parents, seeing our lives in the perspective of generations. And if we were fortunate in our grandparents, we may be reminded of times when we were loved and welcomed simply for being who we are, holding our place on the family ladder.

Or should we think of the generations as a turning wheel? Do we really return to the same family, trading roles with our children's children? Maybe the experiences of Leslie and Sheryl and Iris point to a hidden pattern in life's workings. Leslie's story of Angus and her grandfather has another thought-provoking spin:

> About eight or nine years ago I had an aura reading done. I was told that I had been an Iowa farmer, a town patriarch of sorts, around the turn of the century. Little did I know at that time, but a few years later my genealogist mother sent me a package about my grandfather's family, and guess what my grandfather's father was: an Iowa farmer, town patriarch!

15

Out Of Body?

*I*t's no surprise that anesthesia during birth and newborn time can trigger extraordinary experiences. Anesthesia is not always the easy trip to oblivion it's meant to be; it can induce an altered, dislocated sense of self. With the "psychic-physical web" already loosened by labor and delivery, anesthesia is another stress on an unstable system.

One woman recalls how ether given during childbirth created a change of consciousness unlike her other experiences with anesthetics:

> It was in 1950, during the birth of my first child. At the moment when my child began to be born a mask was clapped over my face and I was given ether. I had a distinct sensation that my consciousness was being split away from the unconscious, that indeed I was being split in two. I fought the mask and before I dropped into unconsciousness I had a firm conviction that I was looking at my own unconscious, its heights and its incredible depths. When I came out of the anesthesia I was filled with wonder at what I had seen.

Sometimes the recovery from anesthesia is a struggle, as Jill describes:

> After the delivery I was scheduled for a tubal ligation. Recovering from the anesthesia was difficult. The nurse told me upon awakening that they had been waiting for me to wake for over two hours. As I was coming to, I felt like I had left on a long journey and the hard part was entering my body and then waking up.

The "journey," with all that it implies about what we are, can transform one's perspective—as it did for Helen twenty-five years ago when her child was born. She writes:

> My altered state of consciousness began during the delivery of my son. I will try to put into words an experience that is beyond words. I had an extremely long labor and difficult delivery—the baby being in the wrong position and having to be turned with forceps. I

was given short sniffs of ether to keep me partly conscious so I could help with the delivery. I remember at the height of the pain I knew beyond a shadow of a doubt I was dying and screamed "I am dying and I am glad"—then they gave me enough ether to knock me out.

At first I was out of my body at the top of the delivery room watching the scene. The doctor was telling the nurse to give me a shot. My blood pressure was dropping. The doctor was struggling with all his strength to deliver the baby. I was keenly aware of everything they all said and was very angry because I was trapped and they knew it.

Then I remember traveling on frequency waves and all these voices kept saying "You're on the waves of ether," and "You're in the ozone," repeating it over and over. I reached a state where it was like a sea of beings (no physical bodies) but I could only see something like eyes and there was an unlimited number of them— and they were giving me information and they were so eager and concerned that I get their message. The only part I remember is "If you want to contact us—" and it was so simple a key word but I have not been able to bring it through. They were extremely helpful and wanted me to stay in contact.

Then I was being whirled in a black tunnel and it was terribly frightening. The next thing I remember was the nurse slapping me, bringing me back into this space, saying, "You have a boy." Then from the waist down I was convulsing and nothing would stop it. I got extremely cold and they treated me for shock. All that was on my mind was that I've got to tell somebody where I've been and what I've experienced—but when I saw my husband and opened my mouth to tell him I realized there wasn't any way ever that I could make him understand what had happened to me.

My son was healthy except for a forceps scar on the temple. When they brought him in and laid him next to me I looked in his eyes and experienced an insight that has never left me. "The Wisdom of the Ages" was there. And a feeling of total inadequacy to care for him came over me. I knew this was a job I could not do well—it was a bigger task than I expected.

I was relieved that he was fine but my prime concern was to try to remember the message the beings gave me. I was not fully back into this reality but no one knew it. I was quiet and contemplative. I remember the first time I looked out the hospital window and I knew I was into another world and there was a pink haze over the world. I announced to my husband I would never have another baby (and I didn't). I thought the experience of childbirth was horrible and said so to the nurses. They said, "Oh! You'll soon forget all the pain," but I was thinking while they said that, "No! You're not going to fool me. I'll always remember."

After coming home I experienced "baby blues" for a month or so. I was still in this altered state that I had been thrown into at childbirth. I was totally baffled by what I had experienced but knew it was of great importance and something I must find out the answers to by myself.

I started searching the library—just to put it briefly I started reading psychology, philosophy, parapsychology and religious books. I had set foot on the spiritual path, and fate brought me two very good friends and my sister to share the spiritual journey with. These three friends and I have researched, studied, and traveled together to Ojai, California, many times to hear and be with J. Krishnamurti.

I have integrated the experience into every area of my life. I feel there are different forms of consciousness all around and we are separated from them by our own limited reality.

Becky Coon was given an anesthetic during a miscarriage, to ease the emotional and physical distress. But it left her with an additional burden of anxiety; she had no context for understanding the state of awareness it induced:

I was five months pregnant and experienced severe labor pains which sent us to the hospital. The labor could not be stopped and within twenty minutes I was taken to the delivery room. I asked the nurse if I was going to miscarry and she replied "yes." To save me from more pain I was given gas.

All of a sudden I felt as though I had left my body and was floating above the operating table and listening to what was going on. I could hear the doctor talking to the nurse telling her about the fact that my husband and I had been trying so hard to get pregnant and it had taken a while and he just felt so bad . . . I heard them say here comes the baby and to give me more gas. They also said there was no need for me to be awake for this.

I could feel the baby coming out but there was no pain and I could feel the occasional touch of a hand on my hand and someone asking me if I was all right but I could not answer. I actually thought I was dead as nothing really meant anything to me, and I began to become frightened because I wanted to know what was going on. But everything was out of my control.

It ended just as strangely as it began. One minute I could hear the doctor and nurses as I was floating on this cloud, and soon all was quiet and reality was there. I felt very drained and unsure. I was in a moment of uncertainty and disbelief.

Soon I was aware that I was back in my room and the nurse was there at my side and I asked if everything was over. She said yes. I asked if we had lost the baby and again she said yes. Then she told me the doctor would be around to explain things later.

My husband joined us and we were asked if we wanted to see our daughter. The nurse explained that sometimes it helps the parents to deal with the loss if they see that the baby was actually there and normal except for coming into the world too soon. This way if they are considering another pregnancy they will know that the miscarriage was not caused by any birth defects. We wanted to see our little girl and we did. She was ten ounces and died when her cord was cut. Her lungs were too immature to handle the stress.

I was still shaky from the experience and didn't tell my husband right away. I was so obsessed with seeing our daughter even though she was not alive that I couldn't handle the thought of anything except to tell my husband how beautiful she was. Soon it did hit me and we both fell apart.

The feeling of what happened stayed with me a long time, and I have always been able to talk about our miscarriage but not about this part of it. I was in fear that there was something wrong with me. I worried I had lost my mind and could not figure if it was a reality that occurred or just a dream while under gas.

This had been our first pregnancy and I had never dreamed that we could lose our baby after we had finally become pregnant. I had never heard of anyone miscarrying before and was very unprepared to handle it. My mind was ready to hide behind anything to avoid the thought of losing our baby. I believe this may have caused my experience.

If Becky had known how natural it is to slow down the impact of painful reality, her moment of detachment might not have caused her so much distress. With and without anesthesia, people create such temporary retreats by exiting from the body's frame of reference.

Do these fractured moments ever harm a woman's ability to connect with her newborn baby? Anita's experience—though it was caused by an analgesic (pain medication) rather than an anesthetic—suggests this may be so. Given morphine in labor, she entered an unpleasant state that she described as being out of body. "I felt physically detached," she said, "as if I were watching the whole experience from outside my body." The dissociated feeling persisted; her baby seemed like a stranger and she experienced deep depression in the following months.

Yet it seems we have a natural tendency to shift the focus this way during labor and in the days after birth, and an ability to do so without the unpleasant side-effects that can occur when anesthesia forces us "out."

~   ~   ~

I vividly remember that feeling
of being a body and, separately, a mind.
And the part of me that was the mind
was very large, very present, very in control.
- Cheryl Lockwood

For Denise Tagan, an experience during the birth of her second child was "a great turning point, the stepping stone to my journey as a person":

My labor started on a Saturday evening, so the midwives were notified and we spent most of Saturday evening very excited, and I felt great and ready, slightly uncomfortable, but very bearable at this point. Into Sunday morning and early afternoon, the contractions came much swifter and faster, taking more and more energy. I was still optimistic the baby would be born that day, sometime.

My house was full of four attendants and my husband. I remember being happy, joking, but very tired and in great pain as time went on, and not much seemed to be moving. I was very concerned about everyone's comfort, and even though I concentrated on my breathing and control, I still wanted to be part of everything else around me. I felt self-conscious, not so much of my nakedness, or openness of my body, as of having so much attention focused on me, as if everyone expected me to perform and I kept stalling my performance by concentrating on others.

Then came midnight. Over twenty-four hours, into thirty and still no baby, not much dilation, but a tremendous urge to push and contractions that were long, hard and excruciating. I stopped making jokes. The baby I thought would be born before midnight was clearly not going to be.

My midwives were gentle and patient. I became whiny and exhausted as I never before felt in my life. Everyone was so tired, they started taking shifts to sleep. I had now one attendant, and even my husband conked out in a chair with a blanket around him. As I look back now, I remember the fear I felt as I saw everyone around go to sleep, without effort, almost like when Dorothy, the Scarecrow, the Lion and the Tin Man fell asleep in the field of poppies and nothing could wake them.

As time went into two, three, four o'clock, the pain was so great and there was absolutely no time in between contractions to get any rest. I felt drugged from fatigue (and of course, I hadn't so much as taken an aspirin).

Each time I would "come back" from a contraction, the time lapse between contractions made me feel as if I had left, wasn't in my body. I'm not really clear where it was that I felt I was, but I was not in the room with my body. It was someplace much deeper. This went on for a while, until at one point, I remember feeling like I might faint, and I was talking almost deliriously to my midwife, and then suddenly, I felt very peaceful.

As I remember it now, it might have been a split second, or an eternity, there was no measure of time, but I suddenly in my peacefulness looked down at a body (me) in a rocking chair, with my nightgown on, saw my attendant, my robe on the bed next to the chair; the whole section of the room that I occupied was very clear to me from a point above, as if I hovered over myself and clearly was looking down at myself in this excruciating pain.

When it was over, it seemed things moved very quickly. My senior midwife determined I had a cervical lip that was not moving on its own, and after some painful intervention, the next stage was able to resume and the baby was born in the next hour.

For a long time after, I was awed by the whole experience, and in time was able to look at it from a more objective point of view that led me to question just what exactly happened. I began to read several books, especially about people who had near-death experiences where they describe themselves as leaving their bodies and seeing themselves outside of their own physical state. I felt strange, almost unique, but scared because I never knew anyone this happened to. However, now it is my most precious experience as I look at it as the answer, the real and personal proof of what lies beyond death and the physical self.

Denise had discovered another dimension of her being. In the days after childbirth, women may have similar experiences—moments when the center of consciousness moves away from the body. One week after giving birth, Lynn Amara lay down next to her sleeping baby to nap, but instead found herself in "an in-between state."

Quite suddenly I felt myself ascending extremely rapidly, leaving my body below—just a minute point. Then I "saw" myself with back turned to "me"; two beings of light came to either side of me and covered me with a cloak (mantle). On the back of the cloak was a question mark made of living light. The light began to move; it formed the image of an eagle with outstretched wings. At this point I was becoming self-conscious and very excited. I plummeted back into my body.

Gerry had been studying metaphysical literature before the birth of her child, and "practicing the suggestions—spiritual guides, higher self, communication with nature devas, and so on." But the following experience came unbidden and startled her with a feeling of being out of control. She attributes it to her "level of fatigue, lack of sleep and disorientation after giving birth":

> While breastfeeding late one evening I left my body and buzzed around the room. I was conscious of the fact I had "departed," so to speak. I began communicating through telepathy with my higher self and got a message about conserving my energy. At the time, I was very exhausted with my newborn and lack of uninterrupted sleep.
>
> I have since kept a journal of my activities and out-of-body experiences and am studying to learn more daily. I find that frequently I know of impending events long before they actually materialize, and when I listen to my intuition (for lack of a better word) I can predict or avoid various situations.

Like Gerry, Elaine found that her experience after childbirth stimulated a deeper interest in exploring other dimensions of awareness:

> The birth of my daughter was my first experience giving birth. It was long, painful and extremely joyous. The labor in total was thirty-six hours. About ten hours of it were fairly painful. About four hours were extremely painful! This was a home birth. I had practiced breathing and so on a little but not enough. The practice went out the window when it got intense. I clung onto my husband almost the whole time! When my daughter was finally born I was exhausted, and so thrilled. I could hardly hold her because I was so tired, but I felt like I would do it all over again in an instant.
>
> I was bleeding fairly heavily. After the placenta came out, I continued to bleed. When I got up with help to go pee, I fainted. The midwives decided I ought to go to the hospital. I had received several shots of Pitocin and drunk herb tea, but they felt I needed more Pitocin IV and fluids. I stayed there overnight. The next day I went home and was on bedrest for a week.
>
> It was during the first few days at home that I experienced being out of my body several times. It was quite disconcerting to me. I was not well-practiced in meditation or other methods of mind-control at the time. Everything was so new—the baby, being in bed, and the tremendous sentimental gushes that took me over.
>
> I could feel myself hovering over my body, when I was awake, and I felt dizzy. Fortunately, a friend who was trained at the Berkeley Psychic Institute came over almost every day to take care of me (and give my husband a break). She was a great listener! She told me this was a common feeling women go through after birthing and she helped me stay grounded. The whole experience encouraged me to explore meditation and gain better control—and enjoy other psychic states.

16

Claire's Story

*T*his is a story of two profoundly healing events, each following a few days after childbirth. With them, we will come to the end of our exploration of the newborn year. Claire writes:

> I am thirty-five years old. I am the mother of two daughters, one of whom is living. Erica is five years old, and Andrea Grace died at birth last spring.
>
> The moving force of my life has been a deep, unquenchable thirst for awareness of "what is." I explored many traditional avenues for growth and gaining knowledge—college, career, travel, reading. I have also explored more untraditional avenues—rebellion, drugs, meditation. Now I identify that deep driving force as the urging of my spirit to move towards God. My family and meditation are my tools in spiritual growth. Right now my main intellectual interest is the growth of awareness and consciousness in children.
>
> I think the cause of my experiences after childbirth was the natural lowering of the individual's constructed defenses at this time. I also think that through a natural sensitivity, enhanced by years of deep meditation, I can sometimes perceive subtle aspects of my environment. Childbirth for me has been a time of acute stress and crisis—both times I felt stripped of my day-to-day self; I felt open and vulnerable beyond anything I'd ever known before, since I had constructed the "me" I live with, anyway.
>
> Erica's birth was horrible. I had developed toxemia, and after several days of hospitalization, I was given a caesarean under general anesthesia. The anesthesia didn't take hold before they started the surgery, so I experienced unbelievable pain. I remember my "being" as an indestructible, tiny speck in a whirling black vortex of pain.
>
> The next two days contained many minor stresses and problems associated with an abnormally high blood pressure. I was kept in intensive care—no visitors—many medical procedures. The third day my blood pressure was so high it was life-threatening. All sorts

of machinery was rolled in and they monitored me constantly. A new specialist was brought in, and he and the other doctors gathered outside to discuss my case. I realized finally that I could die—and all my fear coalesced.

At that moment, I had several deeply spiritual insights—that my life truly was in the hands of God, and I surrendered my will to God's will. If I was to die, so be it. Fear left me. For a year and a half I had already known that my purpose in life was to evolve, to grow in consciousness towards God. But at this time I realized that there was another purpose—to help the evolution of others, as well. It was a kind of spiritual conversion from a purely selfish desire to reach God to one that expanded to the welfare of all people.

At this realization, the entire room filled with a soft, glowing golden light, and I felt a deep peace that flowed through my entire body. The doctors came in soon afterwards, and my blood pressure had already dropped. By evening it was normal.

Although Claire's situation was unusual—a time of extreme personal danger—many stories of newborn time have described the same expansion beyond a self-centered view. At a certain stage, preoccupation with our own personal drama gives way to a growing awareness of a wider reality. Often it is the coming of a child that brings this shift in consciousness. And so for many mothers and fathers, the adventure of being a parent is part of the greater adventure of becoming . . . transparent. Claire's story continues:

Four and a half years later, I gave birth to my second child. It was a VBAC delivery in a birthing room—a long, difficult labor, but with a minimum of interference. Andrea Grace was born, tried to breathe, gasped and coughed, and died.

We spent several hours with her body, and finally went home, exhausted. The next day we were overwhelmed with calls and people coming over. Finally we took the phone off the hook and were alone with our grief and shock.

I had a couple of strange experiences that evening. One was looking at a blanket crumpled in a corner of the room, and clearly seeing my daughter's body wrapped in white on it, her face showing, eyes closed. It disturbed me, and I looked away. Then I heard, in my right ear only, so that I turned in that direction, chanting. It was men's voices, a low soft chanting. It reminded me of monks in a chapel, praying. I felt frightened, uncomfortable. I called my husband in—asked him to move the blanket, and to stay with me.

The next day was just there. We made arrangements for cremation of the body.

The following day was a gorgeous spring morning—and we looked out on all the beauty and felt like we could never again feel that fullness of joy when you enjoy something beautiful, without having a pang of grief obscure it. At noon the funeral home called and told us that the cremation would be started at one P.M. We had a friend come get our four-year-old, and we called my parents. My husband and I and my parents had planned a period of meditation during the cremation.

Bruce and I sat in the bedroom, my parents in the adjoining room. We started to meditate. I felt my mind become very quiet and settled, in just a few moments. Immediately as my mind settled, the image of my baby's face came into my mind. It transformed into the image of a young woman—very much alive, and radiant. She had long dark auburn hair, very beautiful, but her face was so shining, so full of white, shining light, that I really didn't see her features and face as one would another person's. It was more the quality of her being that I saw. And what she communicated, and how.

It was a communication that transcended all senses—it was direct—from heart to heart, or soul to soul. And it was so complete. She knew me—all my emotions, my "me"—she seemed to surround me in a total embrace, total Love. She understood my grief and she gave immeasurable sympathy, yet it didn't detract from a total peace, joy and love that she was expressing.

I knew her instantly. And I was overwhelmed with joy. I asked her, "Andrea, will I ever see you?" and she answered, "Oh, yes!" with a smile and great love. I asked, "Will I know you?" "Yes!" and "Will I ever be able to embrace you?" "Oh, yes!" And she was so earnest, and smiling, and full of tenderness and love. I asked her many more questions. She answered them. We "talked" for about forty-five minutes.

I asked her about what Maharishi had said about a loved one's dying opening one's path to God. She said yes, that was true, and she showed me an open channel from me to herself and her world, and showed how the love would flow through that channel to me. The channel was also like an opened pathway for me to follow—to reach her world and that advanced state of evolution.

She also told me the channel worked another way, and held with it a responsibility. She said the love that came to us must also pass through us and be shared with others. We were to learn about Love, to learn unconditional Love, and give it to others.

I asked her, "Why us? Why are we so special?" She said that we are not special, but that it was our time in our evolution that this experience should come to us. She then said that God's light shines equally on everyone—and that everyone is like a window—only some windows are cleaner than others. Those whose windows are clean will feel the light, and the light will pass through them. I

could feel that our "windows" had been given a great cleaning—
that part of Andrea Grace's gift was the purification she brought
us.

It was the most profound experience of my life. It is impossible to
explain it fully—even impossible to remember fully . . . it's more
that the impact of the experience reached to the depths of my being.
My soul came awake in a way that is impossible to maintain in
ordinary consciousness. I remember much of our conversation; I
even wrote it all down afterwards, about a week later. It's still very
clear in my memory though. The part that is impossible to explain
or "re-experience" is the state of awareness of that time—only that
I know it was real, and joyous beyond my capacity to feel now.

The quality of love that was communicated, given, showered
upon me was beyond measure. Total acceptance, reassurance, tenderness, with a touch of warm humor that amazed and delighted
me.

The eight months since this experience have been both very
beautiful and very difficult. The human side of me, the mother, has
grieved. The loss is staggering sometimes. I have been shaken to
my core. And I have opened. Andrea's gift has become ever more
clear to me. In this is the beauty—such deep peace and joy . . . the
knowledge that I truly am the mother of two—that my second
daughter is a radiantly beautiful being. She never comes to me in
that obvious form of a vision, but over and over again she comes in
the form of that encompassing love; I feel the light of God, and in it
are peace and comfort.

Spiritually, my attitudes have changed. I am acutely aware that
God is Love, and that there are many, many ways that God reaches
out to people with that Love. I think God reaches out to all of us in
the world, to each in the manner that can be received. Meditation
has become less of an end in itself to me. I am more concerned with
life, and Love as it manifests itself in my life.

Sometimes the speed with which my defenses are torn down
frightens me. There is enormous vulnerability and openness. I find
that I need to slow down and integrate. I meditate less now,
although someday I expect to go back to a fuller program. I sometimes have worried about my mental stability—particularly in the
past three months or so. My husband is wonderful; he gives me the
reassurance and support I need, and tells me to let myself "fall
apart" for a while. He helps me realize that what I am so afraid to
let go of are only my own constructions anyway. But I still want to
take it slow—the impact of this whole experience is still occurring,
and my psyche needs time to integrate it with life.

Before this experience, I had been seeing my baby as my child.
After talking with her, I saw her as a being far more advanced

spiritually than I—as a guide and helper who would be in relationship with me throughout my life. I felt almost as if she was my mother, then as if she was my sister. Andrea Grace's birth and death, then the experience of seeing and communicating with her being, allowed me the perspective on motherhood as a timeless, essentially spiritual role.

I became acutely aware that our relationship with our children is from an inner basis of equality: a soul-relationship, a mutual spiritual journey.

AFTERWORD

*O*ur explorations have taken us from the personal to the cosmic and back again. This is the power of the newborn year: we focus on one small face, and touch the universe. We move "deeper into our secret lives" and sometimes lose our way in spaces that seem alien.

Have you seen reflections of your own experiences in these stories? Perhaps you have found another way of looking at them, or have new questions to ask. For there are more questions than conclusions here, and many stories are still untold.

Your comments and personal accounts are welcomed. Please direct them to:

Elisabeth Brutto Hallett
P.O. Box 705
Hamilton, MT 59840

ACKNOWLEDGMENTS

Grateful acknowledgment is made to the following for permission to reprint previously published material:

CHAPTER 1
Page 14, from *"Brad's Birth"* by Sandra Griffin in *Birth and the Dialogue of Love* by Marilyn A. Moran (Leawood, KS, New Nativity Press, 1981).
Page 23, from *Psychological Effects of Motherhood*, page 88, (Praeger Publishers, NY:1980) Reprinted by permission of Greenwood Publishing Group, Inc. All rights reserved.

CHAPTER 2
Page 39, from T. Berry Brazelton and Bertrand G. Cramer, M.D., *The Earliest Relationship*, © 1990 by T. Berry Brazelton and Bertrand G. Cramer. Reprinted with permission of Addison-Wesley Publishing Company Inc.
Page 41, from *Double Vision* © 1985 by Judith Skutch and Tamara Cohen. Published by Celestial Arts, Berkeley, CA..

CHAPTER 4
Page 58, from *"The Other Side of Goldie"* by Ray Errol Fox, *Parade*, February 15, 1987. Reprinted with permission of *Parade*, copyright © 1987.
Page 59, from *Transformation Through Birth*, page 134, by Claudia Panuthos (Bergin & Garvey, 1984). Reprinted by permission of Greenwood Publishing Group, Inc. All rights reserved.

CHAPTER 6
Page 90, from *Dylan Thomas: Poems of Dylan Thomas*. Copyright 1945 by the Trustees for the Copyrights of Dylan Thomas. Reprinted by permisison of New Directions Publishing Corporation.
Page 92, from *Models of Love: The Parent-Child Journey* by Barry Vissell, M.D., and Joyce Vissell, R.N., M.S. Reprinted by permission of Ramira Publishing.
Page 94, from *The Jewel in the Lotus, Meditation II* by Grace Cooke (The White Eagle Publishing Trust, 1973). Reprinted by permission of The White Eagle Lodge, Hampshire, England.

CHAPTER 8
Pages 112-3, reprinted from *Beyond the Brain: Birth, Death and Transcendence in Psychotherapy* by Stanislov Grof by permission of the State University of New York Press, © 1985 State University of New York .

CHAPTER 12
Page 157, from *The Prophet* by Kahlil Gibran. Reprinted by permission of Alfred A. Knopf.

CHAPTER 13
Page 172, from Diane Gregg, *"Psychic Awarenss in Pregnancy and Birth"* (Mothering, Spring 1982). Reprinted by permission of Mothering magazine.

CHAPTER 14
Page 184, from *The Family Bed: An Age-Old Concept in Child Rearing* by Tine Thevenin, published by Avery Publishing Group, Inc., Garden City, N.Y. Reprinted by permission.
Page 195, from *The New Mother Syndrome* by Carol Dix. Reprinted by permission of Doubleday Div. of Bantam, Doubleday, Dell Publishing Group, Inc.

INDEX

INDEX

Elisabeth Brutto Hallett was born in Rome, Italy, into a family with many literary interests. Her father was a journalist with the Associated Press and her mother was a creative writer. Her years as an American schoolgirl overseas gave her a unique perspective on what factors shape an individual's life experiences.

She returned to the States during the tumultuous '60s, obtained her psychology degree from the University of California at Santa Cruz, and later, a nursing degree. A student fellowship in neurosurgery deepened her interst in the relationship between the brain and the mind.

Elisabeth's medical experiences convinced her to follow a course of study assisting people to stay well, as opposed to caring for them only when they were sick. She successfully completed a course for yoga instructors at Indra Devi's Yoga Institute and has taught more than two hundred students at her home in Hamilton, Montana.

She is currently pursuing other writing/research projects and raising a son and a daughter with her husband Nick.

Ask your store to carry our fine line of books or
you may order this book and other fine titles directly from:

THE BOOK PUBLISHING COMPANY
PO Box 99
Summertown, TN 38483

or call: **1-800-695-2241**

A Cooperative Method of Natural Birth Control	$ 6.95
Climate in Crisis:	
The Greenhouse Effect and What We Can Do	$11.95
Ecological Cooking: Recipes to Save the Planet	$10.95
George Bernard Shaw Vegetarian Cookbook	$ 8.95
Judy Brown's Guide to Natural Foods Cooking	$10.95
Kids Can Cook	$ 9.95
Murrieta Hot Springs Vegetarian Cookbook	$ 9.95
The Now & Zen Epicure	
Gourmet Cuisine for the Enlightened Palate	$17.95
The NEW Farm Vegetarian Cookbook	$ 7.95
The Power of Your Plate	$10.95
Shepherd's Purse: Organic Pest Control Handbook	$ 6.95
Spiritual Midwifery (Third Edition)	$16.95
Starting Over: Learning to Cook with Natural Foods	$10.95
The Tempeh Cookbook	$ 9.95
Ten Talents (Vegetarian Cookbook)	$18.95
Tofu Cookery	$14.95
Tofu Quick & Easy	$ 6.95
The TVP Cookbook	$ 6.95
Uprisings: The Whole Grain Bakers' Book	$13.95
Vegetarian Cooking for Diabetics	$10.95

Please add $2 per book for shipping.